GRAMMAR BOOSTER FOR OET NURSING

Language and grammar for effective communication in healthcare settings

BETH MCNALLY AND ANNE MACKENZIE

Grammar Booster for OET Nursing

Language and grammar for effective communication in healthcare settings

Beth McNally and Anne Mackenzie

First published 2018
Reprinted 2022

ISBN number: ISBN 978-0-6482043-0-5

Cover & text design: Dionne Del Rae

Disclaimer

CONTENTS

INTRODUCTION

Grammar Booster for OET Nursing has been designed to support nursing students and healthcare professionals seeking to boost their English language proficiency in the workplace.

Grammar Booster for OET Nursing provides the opportunity to develop more effective communication skills for use in a range of healthcare settings through increased awareness of grammar forms presented and practised in context.

WHO IS THIS BOOK FOR?

Grammar Booster for OET Nursing is ideal for healthcare students and professionals who:

- have a current minimum English language proficiency of Upper Intermediate level. (CEFR B2)
- plan to have their English language proficiency assessed through the Occupational English Test (OET).
- wish to build their confidence to become more effective communicators in the workplace.

WHAT IS THE AIM OF THIS BOOK?

Grammar Booster for OET Nursing aims to consolidate, extend and apply existing grammar knowledge to a range of healthcare settings. It is a user-friendly grammar resource which provides relevant grammar practice tasks designed to enhance overall English language proficiency and help facilitate more effective communication in the workplace.

Grammar Booster for OET Nursing can be used for independent study or adapted for classroom use to support specialised English language nursing courses, including English for Academic Purposes (EAP) for Nursing and OET preparation courses.

It should be noted that while *Grammar Booster for OET Nursing* is a valuable supplementary grammar resource for healthcare students and professionals preparing for the OET, it is neither an OET preparation course, nor a medical textbook.

HOW IS THIS BOOK ORGANISED?

Grammar Booster for OET Nursing offers ten units. Units 1-9 are stand-alone units, each of which addresses a key grammar area that may cause difficulty for learners. Unit 10 consolidates all key grammar areas in Units 1-9 through review practice tasks.

This structure offers flexibility for the independent learner to select and to focus on individual areas requiring development. The classroom teacher may also select appropriate units to supplement core teaching resources to address common areas of need.

Units 1-9 include:

- an introductory setting to showcase the grammar area for development
- a Grammar Boost section to provide examples and explanations.
- practice tasks to develop proficiency in applying the grammar structures to healthcare contexts.
- answer keys for the practice tasks in each unit at the back of the book.

Unit 10 is a Review Unit designed to recycle all key grammar areas explored and practised in Units 1-9.

WHO ARE THE AUTHORS?

The authors are experienced English language specialists who have combined their English language knowledge and teaching and assessment skills to develop a valuable grammar resource, which focuses on the application and practice of familiar grammar forms in specific nursing contexts.

The authors have extensive experience of developing relevant customised teaching and assessment materials to support the wide scope of English courses they have delivered.

Beth McNally: Beth specialises in internationally-recognised English examination preparation and assessment and vocational training. It was while she was developing and teaching an English language course for Diploma of Nursing students (English for Nurses) that she first saw the need for a grammar resource specifically designed for nurses to practise their grammar in realistic nursing settings.

Anne Mackenzie: Anne has a wide-ranging career as an English language teacher, assessor, curriculum designer and education consultant in Australia, the Middle East, Asia and the UK. Anne has developed curriculum for a broad scope of English language courses, including internationally-recognised examination preparation and English for Academic Purposes for Nursing. In discussion with teachers on an EAP for Nursing course, Anne realised the need for a specialised grammar book for nurses.

SETTING: HEALTHY EYES CLINIC

A new patient is registering at the Healthy Eyes Clinic. Notice the *questions* in the box below.

> **What** is your first name?
>
> **What** is your surname? **Can** you **spell** that please?
>
> **What** is your date of birth? **When** were you born?
>
> **What** is your address? **Where do** you **live**?
>
> **What** is your mobile phone number?
>
> **Do** you **have** an email address?
>
> **Why did** you **come** to the clinic today?
>
> **Who** is your referring doctor?
>
> **Did** you **bring** your referral with you today?
>
> **How did** you **hear** about the Healthy Eyes Clinic?

GRAMMAR BOOST 1: FUNCTIONS OF QUESTIONS

Questions have an integral function in effective communication and can be used to:

- initiate and extend conversation and discussion.
- discover new information.
- clarify and confirm instructions and opinions.
- ask for permission to do something.

GRAMMAR BOOST 2: COMMON QUESTION SIGNAL WORDS

Frequently used words and expressions to signal questions include:

- What

What *do you mean? Should I take this medication before meals or after meals?*

What *are the common side effects associated with this treatment?*

- Where

Where can I find the Medical Imaging Department?

- Why

Why have I been referred to a specialist?

- Which

Which staff members have completed the annual Workplace Health and Safety training?

- Who

Who is rostered on night duty next week?

- When

When were the pathology samples sent to the laboratory?

- How, how much, how many, how long

How are you feeling today?

How long will I need to use a mobility aid after the surgery?

How can I keep my dressings dry when I am having a shower?

GRAMMAR BOOST 3: COMMON QUESTION SIGNALS WITHOUT SPECIFIC QUESTION WORDS

- Use of a question mark **?** at the end of a sentence in written text:

    *Are you in pain at the moment**?***
    *Can I take your blood pressure now**?***

- Inversion of the subject and the verb forms:

    Statement: **She is taking prescription** medication for the condition.
    Question: **Is she taking prescription** medication for the condition?

    Statement: **The patient has been advised** to stop smoking.
    Question: **Has the patient been advised** to stop smoking?

- Introduction of an auxiliary with the main verb:

    Statement: It **hurts**. (present simple tense)

    Question: **Does** it **hurt?**

    Statement: My son **drove** me to the clinic yesterday. (past simple tense)

    Question: **Did** your son **drive you** to the clinic yesterday**?**

GRAMMAR BOOST 4: UNDERSTANDING KEY INFORMATION IN QUESTIONS

In order to respond to questions appropriately, it is important to be able to identify key word signals in the questions being asked.

COMMON KEY QUESTION SIGNALS	COMMON KEY ANSWER SIGNALS	QUESTION AND ANSWER EXAMPLES
Why?	because, in order to, so that	**Why** *did you see the doctor?* **Because** *I had a sore throat.*
When/what time?	next week, today, in 3 days' time, yesterday, last month, at 4 o'clock	**When** *are you scheduled for knee surgery?* **Next Tuesday.**
How?	by, through + ing You can.......	**How** *can I change the appointment?* **By calling** *the reception during office hours.* **You can call** *the reception during office hours.*
How much? (dosage)	5 millilitres (ml), 250 milligrams (mg), 2 drops, 1 capsule, 1 suppository, 2 puffs	**How much** *of this cough suppressant should be taken in each dose?* *For an adult,* **10 millilitres.**
How often?	Four times, weekly, not very often, only a few times	**How often** *do you use your inhaler?* *At least* **three times a day.**
How long?	Five months, a week, an hour	**How long** *will he have the cast on his broken ankle?* *The doctor said it will probably be about* **6 weeks.**
Which?	This one, the green one, the ward on the third floor	**Which** *building is the Mental Health Centre?* **It's the one** *on the corner of Swan and River Streets.*

Who?	The doctor, the nurse, the patient, Dr James	**Who** is your specialist? **Dr Nichols.**
Where?	in hospital, outside, from Melbourne	**Where** are you having the x-ray? **In the Medical Imaging Department** of the local hospital.
Do you need…?	Yes, please. No, thanks/ No, thank you.	**Do you need** more pain relief? **Yes, please** - the pain is very strong. **No, thank you** - the pain is not too bad at the moment.
Would you like me to…?	Yes, that would be very helpful. No, I will ask my friend to do it.	**Would you like me to** phone your family for you? **Yes, please** – that would be very helpful. **No, thank you** – I will ask my friend to do it.
Can I/ we/ he…?	Yes, he can. / Of course. No, sorry / unfortunately not.	**Can we have** your written consent to do this procedure? **Yes, of course**, where do I have to sign? **Can I sit** outside today? **No, unfortunately not**. It's raining.
Have they had….?	Yes / No, not yet, never	**Have** the residents **had** morning tea today? **Not yet**, the tea trolley is still being prepared.

PRACTICE 1: MATCHING QUESTIONS AND ANSWERS

SETTING: ACCIDENT AND EMERGENCY - PATIENT 1

A patient has been brought to the hospital by ambulance after an accident at the train station. A nurse is asking the patient for details about the accident. Choose the nurse's questions from the box to match the answers given by the patient and complete the dialogue. An example (0) has been done for you.

The nurse's questions

A   Which injuries are causing you the most discomfort?

B   <u>How did you sustain your injuries?</u>

C   Were you feeling dizzy before you fell?

D   Do you need some pain relief?

E   Can you describe what happened when you fell?

F   Are you taking any regular medication at the moment?

0	Nurse:	**(B) *How did you sustain your injuries?***
	Patient:	**I fell on the escalator at the train station.**
1	Nurse:	_____
	Patient:	Not at all. I was just rushing down the escalator to catch my train.
2	Nurse:	_____
	Patient:	I lost my balance and toppled forward, hitting my face on the escalator step in front of me. I also scraped my knees and lower legs.
3	Nurse:	_____
	Patient:	The bleeding from my mouth is slowing down now, but the cuts on my right leg are very painful.
4	Nurse:	_____
	Patient:	No, I occasionally take paracetamol for headaches, but that's all.
5	Nurse:	_____
	Patient:	Yes, please.
	Nurse:	All right. Here's the doctor now. We are going to give you some pain relief and then the doctor will take a look at your injuries.

SETTING: ACCIDENT AND EMERGENCY - PATIENT 2

A parent has arrived at the Accident and Emergency Department with a young child who is presenting with symptoms of an allergic reaction. A nurse is asking the parent for details about the incident. Choose the nurse's questions from the box to match the answers given by the parent and complete the dialogue.

The nurse's questions

A   Has she been stung by an ant before?

B   Can you describe her reaction today?

C   Was her breathing affected?

D   Why have you brought her to the hospital today?

E   How old is your child?

---

1   Nurse: _____

     Parent: Five.

2   Nurse: _____

     Parent: She was stung on her leg by an ant and I was very worried.

3   Nurse: _____

     Parent: Yes once, but she did not have a serious reaction then.

4   Nurse: _____

     Parent: There was immediate swelling at the site of the sting and red welts appeared on her upper body and face.

5   Nurse: _____

     Parent: Not at first, but on the way to the hospital she started wheezing.

PRACTICE 2: FORMING APPROPRIATE QUESTIONS

Mr Barrett has arrived for an appointment at the orthopaedic specialist's clinic. The nurse is asking him questions about his medical history. Choose the nurse's questions from the box to match the answers given by the patient and complete the dialogue. An example (0) has been done for you.

The nurse's questions

A   When did you start noticing these symptoms?

B   Are you a smoker?

C   Does the pain interfere with your sleeping?

D   What is the best contact number for you?

E   Was that surgery successful?

F   Are you taking any medication at the moment?

G   Who should we contact in an emergency?

H   Why have you come to see the specialist today?

I   What is your address?

J   <u>**What is your full name?**</u>

K   Are there any activities that increase your discomfort?

L   Who is your referring doctor?

M   Have you brought any recent x-rays with you?

N   Do you drink alcohol?

O   Do you exercise regularly?

P   Have you ever had any surgery in the past?

Nurse: Good morning. My name is Sean. I am your nurse today. I am going to start by asking you some questions about yourself.

PERSONAL DETAILS

0   Nurse Sean: **(J)   *What is your full name?***

Patient: **George Barrett.**

1   Nurse Sean: _____

Patient: 35 Fraser Street, Newvale.

2   Nurse Sean: _____

Patient: I'll give you my mobile number.

3	Nurse Sean:	_____
	Patient:	My partner. The phone number is 0724 5566.

LIFESTYLE

4	Nurse Sean:	_____
	Patient:	Not anymore, but I used to be.
5	Nurse Sean:	_____
	Patient:	Yes, I like to have a glass of wine with dinner occasionally.
6	Nurse Sean:	_____
	Patient:	I sometimes go swimming at the local pool, but I don't have a regular routine.

MEDICAL HISTORY

7	Nurse Sean:	_____
	Patient:	Dr Yu.
8	Nurse Sean:	_____
	Patient:	Because I have swelling and stiffness in my left knee.
9	Nurse Sean:	_____
	Patient:	About two years ago.
10	Nurse Sean:	_____
	Patient:	The pain is worse if I stand for a long time or walk around a lot.
11	Nurse Sean:	_____
	Patient:	Sometimes the pain keeps me awake at night.
12	Nurse Sean:	_____
	Patient:	Yes, I take anti-inflammatory medication when my knee is very swollen.
13	Nurse Sean:	_____
	Patient:	Yes, I have. I had arthroscopic surgery about 15 years ago to remove some loose fragments of bone from the right knee joint.
14	Nurse Sean:	_____
	Patient:	Yes, it was. I haven't had any further problems with the right knee since then.
15	Nurse Sean:	_____
	Patient:	Yes, here you are. These were taken about two weeks ago.
	Nurse Sean:	Thank you, very much. The doctor will be in to examine you shortly.

PRACTICE 3: FORMING QUESTIONS AND CHOOSING APPROPRIATE ANSWERS

SETTING: NURSING POSITION INTERVIEW

You are on the panel to interview nurses who have applied for a recently advertised nursing position in the local hospital. Formulate the interviewer's questions using the word prompts given. Then select the most appropriate interviewee response from the box for each question. An example (0) has been done for you.

A	By reading reports on the latest nursing practices and by attending seminars in the field.
B	To establish a diabetes education clinic in my local community.
C	Yes, I would like to learn more about diabetes management.
D	I am hard-working, enjoy helping people and have relevant nursing experience in this area.
E	For about 4 years.
F	<u>Because I have always been interested in helping sick people.</u>
G	I really enjoy the challenge of working with many different people.

---

0 did / why / a / become / nurse / decide / to / you?

Question: **Why did you decide to become a nurse?**

Answer: **(F)** *Because I have always been interested in helping sick people.*

1 been / nurse / have / how / you / long / a ?

Question: _____

Answer: _____

2 most / do / what / nurse / like / about / you / working / a / as ?

Question: _____

Answer: _____

3 qualities / personal / bring / this / to / skills / what / you / would / and / position?

Question: _____

Answer: _____

4 specialise / plan / the / do / in / particular / in / you / to / any / future / area ?

Question: _____

Answer: _____

5   you / latest / nursing / do / about / how / in / advances / learn / the ?

    Question: _____

    Answer: _____

6   long-term / what / your / goals / are / professional ?

    Question: _____

    Answer: _____

PRACTICE 4: IDENTIFYING KEY INFORMATION IN QUESTIONS AND CHOOSING APPROPRIATE ANSWERS

Read the following questions and answers carefully. Look for key signals in each question and choose the most suitable answer A, B or C. An example (0) has been done for you.

0   How are you getting home from the clinic today?

    A   I go for regular walks.

    B   <u>My son will collect me.</u>

    C   I came in a taxi.

1   What should I call you?

    A   Mrs Shaw.

    B   At 6 o'clock.

    C   My number is 5532 4000.

2   What time is it?

    A   There is time to have a shower before lunch.

    B   I know it is time.

    C   It is almost midnight.

3   When will you come back?

    A   I saw you earlier.

    B   Yes, thank you.

    C   After I have spoken to the doctor.

4   Do you take any over-the-counter medications?

    A   Yes, an antihistamine.

    B   I have not been to the pharmacy.

    C   I have a prescription.

5   When was the last time your dressing was changed?

    A   The community nurse can change it for me.

    B   2 days ago.

    C   No.

6   How much sleep did you have last night?

    A   About 11.30pm.

    B   8 hours or so.

    C   Well, thanks.

7   Does it hurt when you urinate?

    A   Yes, I have.

    B   Yes, I do.

    C   Yes, it does.

8   Do you know the way to the clinic?

    A   By car.

    B   Yes, I have been there before.

    C   I will be on time.

PRACTICE 5: IDENTIFYING KEY INFORMATION IN ANSWERS AND CHOOSING APPROPRIATE QUESTIONS

Read the following questions and the answer carefully. Look for key signals in the answer and choose the most suitable question A, B or C. An example (0) has been done for you.

0   ANSWER: It is not too bad. It is about a 4.

    A   Do you have any pain?

    B   <u>Can you rate your pain on a scale of one to ten?</u>

    C   Where is the pain?

1   ANSWER: It is for my heart.

    A   Do you have a prescription for this medication?

    B   Did you take this medication this morning?

    C   Why do you take this medication?

2   ANSWER: Three.

    A   How many times have you checked your blood sugar level today?

    B   How often do you check your blood sugar level?

    C   When did you last check your blood sugar level?

3   ANSWER: No. I have to collect it.

    A   Does the pharmacy deliver your prescription medication?

    B   Can you walk to the pharmacy?

    C   Is the pharmacy far from you?

4   ANSWER: Yes, she has just been.

    A   Have you been given your Letter of Discharge?

    B   Who is going to stay with you overnight?

    C   Have you seen the doctor this morning?

5   ANSWER: Yes, please. I can't see clearly without them.

    A   Have you cleaned your glasses?

    B   Can I help you to find your glasses?

    C   Where are your glasses?

6   ANSWER: About 5 weeks ago.

    A   Are you in pain at the moment?

    B   When did the pain start?

    C   How long have you had this pain?

7   ANSWER: This morning.

    A   Do you need to move your bowels?

    B   Do you move your bowels regularly?

    C   When did you last move your bowels?

8   ANSWER: Yes, it is too hot in here.

    A   Would you like me to turn off the heating?

    B   Would you like another blanket for your bed?

    C   Is it all right if I close the window?

SETTING: COMMUNITY CHILD HEALTH CLINIC

A father of two young children has asked nurse Annette Wu to recommend items for a first aid kit. Here are her suggestions. Notice the *nouns* in bold below. Think about whether they are countable or uncountable.

antiseptic **soap**	a cold **pack**	burn **gel**
antibacterial **wipes**	**scissors** and **tweezers**	anti-itch **ointment**
adhesive **plasters**	a digital **thermometer**	insect **repellent**
gauze roller **bandages**	splinter **probes**	children's **paracetamol**
sterile gauze **pads**	**sunscreen**	prescription **medication**
adhesive **tape**	**saline**	

GRAMMAR BOOST 1: COUNTABLE NOUNS

Countable nouns (patient, ward, bandage, eye, test, tumour)

• have both a singular and a plural form

*We have a new **patient** arriving this morning.*
*There are **patients** waiting for treatment in triage.*

• can take a singular or a plural verb

*This **patient** needs to be seen urgently.*
*These **patients** need to be seen urgently.*

• can be used with numbers

*Four **patients** are ready for discharge.*

BOOSTER TIP - TYPICAL COUNTABLE NOUNS

Countable nouns are often found in the following categories:

1   Jobs - physiotherapist, podiatrist, paediatrician, community nurse, lactation consultant

2   Instruments - stethoscope, dropper, catheter, pacemaker, syringe

3   Surgical procedures - transplant, appendectomy, arthroscopy, caesarean section

4   Medical complaints in or on a part of the body - ulcer, cataract, abrasion, sprain, bruise

5   Parts of the body - leg, thigh, cheek, kidney, artery, vein, limb, organ

---

GRAMMAR BOOST 2: UNCOUNTABLE NOUNS

Uncountable nouns (information, equipment, advice, harm, damage, research, news, rehabilitation)

- do not have a plural form

*I will give you some **information** on vaccination.*

- take a singular verb

*This **information** needs to be given to the specialist.*

- cannot be used with numbers, however, quantity can often be described using special phrases

*Several pieces of **information** were missing from the Letter of Discharge.*

BOOSTER TIP - TYPICAL UNCOUNTABLE NOUNS

Uncountable nouns are often found in the following categories:

1 Materials/substances - gauze, water, oxygen, iron, magnesium, vitamin D, morphine, blood

2 Feelings - happiness, hope, honesty, anger, depression, anxiety

3 Activities - work, help, research, sleep, housework

4 Abstract ideas - health, hygiene, progress

5 Groups of items - equipment, clothing, money, cash, jewellery

6 Medical conditions and illnesses - gastritis, hypertension, tonsillitis, diabetes, osteoporosis, asthma, arthritis, pneumonia, malaria

7 Fields of study - nursing, medicine, biology, pharmacology, dentistry

---

GRAMMAR BOOST 3: NOUNS WHICH ARE BOTH COUNTABLE AND UNCOUNTABLE

Some nouns can be both countable and uncountable, depending on how they are used. Compare:

Countable: *I have **a** sharp **pain** in my abdomen.*
Uncountable: *He is not in any **pain**.*

Countable: *It looks like **an** ingrown **hair**.*
Uncountable: *People often lose their **hair** during chemotherapy.*

Countable: *You have **a** small skin **cancer** on your nose.*
Uncountable: *You have lung **cancer**.*

Countable: *Could you help Mrs Smith book **a time** to come back and see me?*
Uncountable: *Do you have **time** to help me?*

Countable: *The doctor has prescribed **a** new **medication** for your cough.*
Uncountable: *He is on **medication** to manage his stress and anxiety.*

Countable: *Do you think my daughter has **an** ear **infection**?*
Uncountable: *There is a risk of **infection** after surgery.*

GRAMMAR BOOST 4: GROUP NOUNS

1   Some nouns can take a singular or a plural verb. Both are correct.

*The staff **has** been told about the fire drill today./ The staff **have** been told about the fire drill today.*
*The family **was** notified./ The family **were** notified.*

As a general rule, if you think of the group as a whole group, use the singular verb. If you think of each individual, separate member of the group, use the plural verb.

2   Some nouns are always plural.

Some nouns are always plural, for example, *forceps, scissors, tweezers, glasses* and *trousers*. They take a plural verb.

Pass me the forceps. The tweezers are on the tray. Are the scissors in the drawer?

They can also be used with the phrase *a pair* of and take a singular verb.

*Where **are** the scissors? They **are** in the drawer. OR There **is** a pair (of scissors) in the drawer.*

Contents, belongings and *surroundings* also take a plural verb.

*The contents of the residents' files **are** confidential.*

*Your belongings **need** to be stored in the bedside cabinet.*

*The patient's surroundings **are** unfamiliar as he has just been moved to a new room.*

PRACTICE 1: IDENTIFYING COUNTABLE AND UNCOUNTABLE NOUNS 1

Look at the nouns in the box. Decide whether they are countable, uncountable or both. Then write them in the correct column in the table. An example has been done for you.

dentist tumour syringe lung pain vitamin B prescription calcium thermometer nebuliser mask diverticulitis hair medication acne cell bone

COUNTABLE	UNCOUNTABLE	BOTH
dentist		

PRACTICE 2: IDENTIFYING COUNTABLE AND UNCOUNTABLE NOUNS 2

Decide whether the underlined nouns in each sentence are countable (c) or uncountable (u). Write your answer in the brackets ( ). An example (0) has been done for you.

Pre-operative preparation

0   All patients meet with a <u>nurse</u> (**c**) prior to <u>surgery</u> (**u**).

1   The patient's health history and personal <u>details</u> (   ) are carefully checked.

2   Vital signs are recorded, including <u>blood pressure</u> (   ), <u>pulse</u> (   ) and temperature.

3   The patient is able to ask any questions about the <u>procedure</u> (   ) and ask for <u>information</u> (   ) on post-operative recovery.

Cardiac rehabilitation

1   Cardiac <u>rehabilitation</u> (   ) is recommended for <u>patients</u> (   ) who have suffered a <u>heart attack</u> (   ) or other cardiac event.

2   Cardiac rehabilitation programs have been shown to assist patients to resume normal daily activities sooner after cardiac <u>procedures</u> (   ).

3   <u>Participation</u> (   ) in cardiac rehabilitation is also thought to improve patients' psychological <u>well-being</u> (   ).

4   <u>Participants</u> (   ) also experience a lower risk of recurrent cardiac events compared with those who do not join a cardiac rehabilitation program.

PRACTICE 3: CHOOSING APPROPRIATE FOLLOW-ON SENTENCES

Match the sentences in column A with the most suitable follow-on sentence in column B. Write your answers in the space provided. An example (0) has been done for you.

COLUMN A	COLUMN B
0 <u>Your finger has blood on it.</u>	A Could you get me a pair?
1 These bedclothes have been soiled.	B They are in the dining room.
2 I need some scissors.	C They are severe.
3 I need a kidney dish.	D Please wash them.
4 Do you know where the nurse is?	E It is severe.
5 Do you know where the staff are?	F I will put it back in the cupboard.
6 He has pains in his abdomen.	G Could you get me one?
7 He has pain in his left shoulder.	H I will label them.
8 This equipment is no longer needed.	I I will return it to the pharmacist for disposal.
9 These instruments have been sterilised.	J They are used to treat depression.
10 This medication is out of date.	K <u>Please wash it.</u>
11 These medications are new.	L I will put them away.
12 Your name needs to be on your belongings.	M He is in the office.

Write your answers here.

0	1	2	3	4	5	6	7	8	9	10	11	12
K												

SETTING: ST JOAN'S NURSING HOME

Nursing home resident Mr Robert Turner, aged 83 years, recently had a fall. Nurse Rita Sanchez is reading today's report in Mr Turner's file. Notice the *nouns and articles (a, an, the)* in the excerpt below.

> **Mr Turner** fell in **the corridor** at 1000. **The doctor** on call confirmed **a fracture** of **the** left **femur**. The nurse took **observations** and **an ambulance** was called. Mr Turner's private doctor and family were notified. He was transferred to **St Vincent's Hospital** at 1100.

GRAMMAR BOOST 1: A / AN

A / an is used with singular countable nouns:

A   when mentioning something for the first time
      *I need to have **an** endoscopy. The doctor has scheduled the endoscopy for Friday.*

B   with jobs or roles
      ***a** social worker, **an** occupational therapist*

C   to describe an aspect of a thing in general e.g. what it is used for, what it looks like
      ***A** scalpel is used to make **an** incision.*

D   to mean one single thing
      ***a** towel, **a** hoist, **an** ulcer, **a** headache*

E   to mean each/every or per
      *10 millilitres **an** hour, 8 paracetamol **a** day*

PRACTICE 1: MATCHING FUNCTIONS OF *A* AND *AN*

Choose the most suitable explanation (A-E) from Grammar Boost 1 to describe the function of *a* and *an* (in *italics*) in each sentence. An example (0) has been done for you.

0   He is *a cardiologist*. **(B)**

1   The x-ray showed that I have a *dislocated shoulder*. (   )

2   *A glucometer* measures blood glucose levels. (   )

3   The doctor does rounds once *a day*. (   )

4   There is *a playground* in the hospital garden. (   ) Volunteers supervise the playground between 8am and 5pm.

GRAMMAR BOOST 2: THE

The is used:

A   with things which have been previously mentioned
*I need to have an endoscopy. The doctor has scheduled **the** endoscopy for Friday.*

B   when the audience knows which thing or person is being referred to
*Ask **the** nurse. Call **the** midwife.*

C   with plural place names and place names which include a noun
***the** Philippines, **the** United Kingdom*

D   with superlative adjectives
***the** fastest, **the** deepest, **the** worst, **the** least, **the** most*

E   with ordinal numbers
***the** second, **the** third, **the** twenty-sixth*

PRACTICE 2: MATCHING FUNCTIONS OF *THE*

Choose the most suitable explanation (A-E) from Grammar Boost 2 to describe the function of *the* (in *italics*) in each sentence.

1   There is a playground in the hospital garden. Volunteers supervise *the playground* between 8am and 5pm. (   )

2   This is *the best* way to do it. (   )

3   She is originally from *the Netherlands* but has lived here for 35 years. (   )

4   Can you call *the social worker*? (   )

5   We will see you on *the fourth* of August. (   )

GRAMMAR BOOST 3: NO ARTICLE

No article is used with **plural** or **uncountable** nouns:

A   to mention something for the first time
***Rehabilitation** plays an important part in recovery from major surgery.*

B   to talk about things in general
    Osteoporosis *mostly affects older* **people**.

C   with place names
    Sydney, Beijing, Manilla, India, Australia, New Zealand, East Brisbane

D   with days of the week
    Monday, Friday

E   with months of the year
    June, September

F   with names of institutions
    Westmead Hospital, St John's Nursing Home

G   with people's names
    John Cooper, Mrs Hunter, Kayoko Shinozawa, Mr Chiesa

H   with names of meals
    breakfast, morning tea, lunch, afternoon tea, dinner

PRACTICE 3: MATCHING FUNCTIONS OF NOUNS WITHOUT ARTICLES

Choose the most suitable explanation (A-H) from Grammar Boost 3 to describe the function of *nouns* (in *italics*) being used without articles in each sentence.

1   Public hospital *wait lists* are constantly monitored. (   )

2   She had a hysterectomy in *April*. (   )

3   *Dinner* will be served in the dining room at 6pm. (   )

4   There is a nursing home in *West End*. (   )

5   *Digital mammography equipment* was donated to the breast clinic. (   ) The equipment is useful in diagnosing breast abnormalities in younger women.

6   This is *Marian Allan*. She is 71 years old. (   )

7   He was transferred to *St Paul's Hospice* yesterday. (   )

8   Your mother is coming in for respite on *Thursday*, is that correct? (   )

What is the difference? *In the hospital* and *in hospital*

To be *in hospital* means to be there for treatment; the purpose/function of the building is important.

My father is in hospital. (He is sick and needs hospital treatment.)

In/at the hospital means someone or something is located there.

There is a pharmacy in the hospital. (It is located there.)

I work at the local hospital. (It is my place of work.)

PRACTICE 4: COMPLETE THE SENTENCE

Use a / an, the or --- (no article) to complete the sentences. An example (0) has been done for you.

0 We will see you again in   ---   May.

1 Can you rate _____ pain on _____ scale of one to ten?

2 You have _____ small, decubitus ulcer on your thigh.

3 This medication belongs to _____ Jin Hee Sook.

4 Mr Singh had _____ laparoscopic cholecystectomy last night.

5 It looks like _____ eczema.

6 Dr Lee has _____ Thursday off, so Dr Gale will be in to see you.

7 Miss Petrovic presented to _____ Emergency Department yesterday afternoon.

8 _____ first dose can be taken this evening.

9 Your child will need _____ x-ray so we can check if the fracture is healing correctly.

10 The Director of Nursing worked in aged care in _____ United States before coming here.

11 We are training nurses from _____ Nepal, _____ China and _____ Philippines.

12 _____ gastroenterologist is someone who specialises in diseases of the digestive system.

13 _____ ophthalmologists specialise in medical and surgical eye problems.

14 He will need checking once _____ hour.

15 The surgeon achieved _____ best outcome for the patient.

16 Remember to take your medication with _____ dinner.

17 _____ research is being done on brain tumours which doctors hope will result in better treatment options.

18 There is a neonatal intensive care unit in _____ hospital.

PRACTICE 5: ERROR CORRECTION

Each of the following sentences contains one extra word which should not be there. Identify the word and write it on the line provided at the end of the sentence. An example (0) has been done for you.

0   Mrs Jones is in **the** pain.   ___the___

1   If your symptoms persist, please see your doctor for an advice.   _____

2   He is making a good progress after the surgery.   _____

3   That is a very strange behaviour for him.   _____

4   The life with a disability can be difficult.   _____

5   He would like to work as a nurse in the Melbourne.   _____

6   Have you had the lunch, yet?   _____

PRACTICE 6: CLOZE

Read the following Letter of Discharge. Complete each space with a/an, the or --- (no article) to complete each sentence. An example (0) has been done for you.

Mr William Parker
Director of Nursing
Cherry Park Nursing Home
25 Duke Avenue
Arlinghurst

14 April (year)

Re: Mrs Amita Kaur, aged 80 years

Dear Mr Parker

Mrs Kaur was admitted to St Joseph's Hospital on 10 April with **(0) a** suspected fracture of the right hip. This was confirmed by x-ray. She underwent surgery on 10 April. She is now ready for discharge back into your care.

Antibiotics and (1)_____ analgesic were given intravenously for 24 hours following surgery. Mrs Kaur requires (2)_____ pain relief as necessary as ordered by the medical officer. Currently, she is taking paracetamol 3 times (3)_____ day for pain management and oral antibiotics (see medication chart). Her routine medications remain unchanged.

(4)_____ physiotherapist introduced Mrs Kaur to sitting and standing exercises on 11/4. On 12/4, she commenced short walks around (5)_____ ward on a wheelie walker with the support of a physical therapist. She requires (6)_____ wheelchair for long distances. She has limited mobility and requires (7)_____ assistance with showering, toileting, walking and transfers. Please organise your physiotherapist and occupational therapist to assess Mrs Kaur for (8) _____ equipment to aid function.

Please monitor (9)_____ wound for signs of infection and remove the sutures in seven days.

Mrs Kaur is making good progress and will return to (10) _____ care home today.

Please contact me if you have any queries.

Yours sincerely

Nurse in Charge
St. Joseph's Hospital

DETERMINERS and QUANTITIES

SETTING: ON THE WARD

James Parson has been in a workplace accident and has just been transferred from the Emergency Department to the ward. Nurse Stephanie Shimada is talking to Mrs Parson about her husband's condition. Notice the **determiners** in bold.

> He has **several** abrasions on his torso and **some** grazes and bruising to his chest and back. He has a deep cut on his left lower leg which requires stitching and **another** superficial laceration on his right lower leg. **All** of his wounds have been assessed. There does not appear to be **any** nerve damage. There are **no** signs of trauma to the head and **no** internal injuries or internal bleeding. He has been given pain relief so he is not experiencing **any** discomfort at the moment. **None** of his injuries are life-threatening but he may take **several** weeks to fully recover. He will need rest and possibly rehabilitation prior to returning to work. There is **some** risk of infection in the short term but overall there is **little** risk of ongoing problems or complications. You can see him in **a few** minutes. You will be able to spend **a little** time with him before visiting hours end, but do not expect **much** conversation from him as the medication has made him drowsy. He can have visitors tomorrow, but not too **many** at once.

GRAMMAR BOOST 1: DETERMINERS USED TO TALK ABOUT QUANTITIES

Determiners are used to describe nouns. Common determiners used to talk about quantities include: *much, many, some, any, a little, a few, little, few, another, several, none, no, all* and *several*.

Look at the examples below to see how these determiners are used with countable and uncountable nouns.

DETERMINERS + COUNTABLE NOUNS	DETERMINERS + UNCOUNTABLE NOUNS
Many *He should not have too **many visitors**.*	Much *He does not seem to be making **much progress** at the moment.*
A few *You can see him in **a few minutes**.*	A little *We require **a little** more **information** from the safety officer at his workplace.*

Few *He had **few belongings** on his person when he arrived.*	**Little** *There is **little risk** of ongoing problems.*
Some *He has **some grazes** on his chest.*	**Some** *He has **some bruising** to his chest and back.*
None ***None of his injuries** are life threatening*	**None** ***None of the equipment** has been replaced.*
No *There are **no signs** of trauma to the head.*	**No** *There has been **no** further **research** in this area*
Any *Are there **any plastic surgeons** available?*	**Any** *There does not appear to be **any nerve damage**.*
All ***All of his wounds** have been carefully examined.*	**All** *Will **all of his rehabilitation** be done at the hospital?*
Several *He has **several abrasions** on his torso.*	
Another *There is **another** superficial **laceration** on his right lower leg.*	

PRACTICE 1: COMPLETE THE SENTENCE 1

Choose the most suitable word to complete the sentences below. An example (0) has been done for you.

Any or **some**?

0   Does Mrs Tewksbury have __**any**__ pills left? If not, I will need to call the pharmacy.

1   I have _____ ointment for your insect bite.

2   I do not have _____ crutches available for hire. I will call another pharmacy for you.

3   Mrs Dawson has a headache. Can you give her _____ paracetamol, please?

4   Do you have _____ pre-existing medical conditions?

5   He does not seem to have _____ cognitive impairment following the stroke.

Much or **many**?

1 How _____ millilitres of urine has he passed?

2 Mrs Mitchell is not doing _____ exercise at the moment. Her doctor has suggested that she goes for a daily walk.

3 There is not _____ movement in Peter Farmer's hand.

4 There can be _____ different causes of abdominal pain.

5 How _____ water have you drunk today?

Few or **little**?

1 Mrs Brown has _____ chance of falling pregnant naturally. She is going to explore her options.

2 This medication has _____ serious side effects.

3 There are _____ documented cases of this disease so it is very difficult to access information about it.

4 Very _____ information is available about this new drug because it is still being trialled.

A few or **a little**?

1 Mr Khan has _____ concerns about his treatment.

2 Mrs Doherty ate _____ yoghurt at breakfast this morning. Her appetite is increasing.

3 Ms Hutton said there were _____ times last week when she felt faint.

4 You have _____ free time before the group exercise class starts at 11.00am.

PRACTICE 2: COMPLETE THE SENTENCE 2

Choose and <u>underline</u> the most suitable word in each sentence. An example (0) has been done for you.

0 *<u>All</u>/Any* of the embryos had chromosomal abnormalities.

1 How *many/much* different inhalers do you use?

2 *No/None* of the embryos survived the transfer.

3 He regained *all/a few* of the feeling in his finger following the accident.

4 Is he taking *any/all* anti-psychotic medication?

5 *No/None* prescription medication can be given without authorisation from a doctor.

6 *Few/Any* infections are as serious as this one.

7 Do you feel *any/all* tingling in your leg?

8 How *many/much* assistance does Mr Watanabe need with showering and dressing?

9 *Every/All* staff member is required to be vaccinated against influenza annually.

10 *Some/Any* of the residents require a medication review.

11 Mr Douglas needs *a little/a few* more reassurance.

12 The residents of the hostel require assistance with *many/much* activities of daily living.

PRACTICE 3: MULTIPLE CHOICE CLOZE

Read the following excerpt from a brochure. Choose the most suitable answer A, B, C or D to complete the text below. An example (0) has been done for you.

INJURY REHABILITATION WITH EVERCARE PHYSIOTHERAPY CLINIC

Evercare Physiotherapy specialises in the management of injury rehabilitation. We specialise in injuries of the spine, knee and back as well as specific sport-related injuries.

We treat patients of **(0) all** ages. We work with you to develop a plan to support your recovery.

Following a physical examination, your therapist will prescribe exercises which aim to reduce pain, build strength and assist you to regain any lost mobility. We will determine how (1) _____ assistance and support you will need to follow your programme and involve other health professionals if necessary.

Your recovery may only take (2)_____ days and require (3)_____ medical supervision. On the other hand, especially in the case of serious injury, your recovery may involve (4)_____ months of therapy. (5)_____ adjustments to your lifestyle may be recommended to aid your recovery.

All therapists who work with you will give you a personalised programme to take home. You will be able to work on (6)_____ exercises at home on your own. You do not need (7)_____ specialised equipment to perform your exercises at home.

Patients often see signs of improvement within (8)_____ sessions.

(9)_____ referral is necessary. We conduct an initial assessment at your first appointment.

If you have (10)_____ questions about our services, please do not hesitate to call.

0	**A** some	**B** **all**	**C** much	**D** little
1	**A** many	**B** a little	**C** much	**D** few
2	**A** some	**B** many	**C** a little	**D** a few
3	**A** little	**B** few	**C** many	**D** any
4	**A** all	**B** many	**C** much	**D** few
5	**A** All	**B** Some	**C** Few	**D** Much
6	**A** many	**B** much	**C** none	**D** a little
7	**A** some	**B** any	**C** many	**D** little
8	**A** a few	**B** few	**C** a little	**D** many
9	**A** None of the	**B** None	**C** Any	**D** No
10	**A** all	**B** few	**C** any	**D** a little

GRAMMAR BOOST 2: COMMON EXPRESSIONS TO DESCRIBE PACKAGING AND MEASURES OF MEDICATIONS AND MEDICAL SUPPLIES

A   Medications and medical supplies - Packaging

a **bottle** of cough syrup

a **box** of incontinence pads

a **packet** of gauze

a **roll** of tape

a **sachet** of urinary alkaliser/nasal wash/osmotic laxative/antibacterial cleansing wipes

a **tube** of salve/ointment/gel/cream/linament

a **vial** of sterile water

B   Medications and medical supplies – Measures

a **course** of antibiotics

a **dose** of medicine

a **metered** dose of medication

a **puff** of aerosol/nasal spray

a **drop** of saline

a **scoop** of powdered baby formula

a **spray** of nasal decongestant

a **swab** of antiseptic

a **unit** of blood

GRAMMAR BOOST 3: COMMON EXPRESSIONS USED TO DESCRIBE MEASUREMENT, QUANTITIES, AGE AND FREQUENCY

Heart rate - beats per minute
His resting heart rate is 75 **beats per minute***.*

Pulse rate - beats per minute
Her pulse rate is 86 **beats per minute***.*

Temperature - degrees Celsius
*Her temperature is 39.6***°C***.*

Respiration rate - breaths per minute

His respiration rate is 22 **breaths per minute.**

Weight - grams, kilograms

She weighs 8.3 **kilograms**.

Height - centimetres, metres

He is 182 **centimetres** tall.
He is 1.82 **metres** tall.

Length - millimetres, centimetres

There was a splinter measuring 6 **millimetres** in the palm of her hand.
She has a 10 **centimetre** scar on her abdomen.
The baby measured 59 **centimetres** in length.

Depth - millimetres, centimetres

Carl York's puncture wound is 3 **centimetres** deep.

Size - millimetres, centimetres

The mole measures **4 millimetres** by **7 millimetres**.
The heat patch is **7 centimetres** by **12 centimetres**.

Age - minutes, days, weeks, years

The oxygen tubes were removed when she was 17 **days** old.
He is 46 **years** old.
Thank you for seeing Ms Fisher, aged 33 **years**.

Length of time - seconds, minutes, hours, days, weeks, months, years

I need you to hold your breath for about 10 **seconds**.
I will come back to check on you in about 20 **minutes**.
The giving set is 20 drops per minute given over 2 **hours**.
This course of antibiotics takes 7 **days** to complete.
Thomas Chin has been bedridden for a **week**.
I have had this cough for several **months**.
She has been taking a blood thinning medication for almost **3 years**.

Liquids - drops, millilitres, litres, units

Put 2 **drops** of saline in each eye every night before bed.
The giving set is 20 **drops** per minute.
Take 7.5 **millilitres** every 12 hours with food for 5 days.
The stock strength is 25000 **units** in 5 **millilitres**.

Solids - micrograms, milligrams, grams, kilograms

Each spray contains 125 **micrograms** of drug A.
This ointment contains 10 **milligrams** per **gram** of drug H.

*Each capsule contains 2 **milligrams** of drug P.*

*This suspension contains 48 **milligrams** per millilitre of drug M.*

*Mr Wong has been prescribed 15 **milligrams** of drug E subcutaneously.*

*The stock strength is 125 **milligrams** in 5 millilitres.*

Frequency - a, every, per

*Are you using your inhaler twice **a** day?*

*You need to change the dressing **every** 3 days.*

*Hemodialysis is usually done 3 or more times **per** week.*

PRACTICE 4: MATCHING QUESTIONS AND RESPONSES

Choose the most suitable response from Column B for each question in Column A. Write your answers in the space provided. An example (0) has been done for you.

COLUMN A	COLUMN B
0 <u>How long have you had this pain?</u>	A 5 or 6 times.
1 How much blood was Mr Lo transfused?	B 176 centimetres.
2 How much nasal spray do I use?	C 73 kilograms.
3 Are there any incontinence pads in the cupboard?	D **About a month.**
4 How much baby formula do I use?	E 3 units.
5 How much sterile water do you need to wash the wound?	F 2 puffs in each nostril, once a day.
6 How much saline do I put in each eye?	G Yes, 6 boxes.
7 How tall are you?	H 37.1°C.
8 How many times a day do you pass urine?	I 4 vials.
9 What do you weigh?	J About 45 seconds.
10 How long did the seizure last?	K 2 drops.
11 How often do you reposition Mrs Wilson?	L Every 2 hours.
12 How many antiseptic wipes are in the packet?	M 70 beats per minute.
13 What is his pulse rate?	N 1 level scoop.
14 What is her temperature?	O 5 sachets in each packet.

Write your answers here.

0	1	2	3	4	5	6	7	8	9	10	11	12	13	14
D														

PRACTICE 5: COMPLETE THE SENTENCE

Choose the most suitable word from the box to complete each passage A-L. An example (0) has been done for you.

Passage A

beats   breaths   °C

On examination, Eileen King's temperature was 38.2 **(0)** _°C_, her pulse rate was 100

(1)_____ per minute and her respiration rate was 30 (2)_____ per minute.

Passage B

millilitres   times   hours   minute

Seven-year-old Samantha Harris vomited six (1)_____ over a nine hour period. No blood was detected in the vomit. She cannot keep any fluids or solids down. We will attempt to rehydrate orally, at two (2)_____ per (3)_____ for three (4) _____ . If that does not work, we will replace lost fluids and salts intravenously.

Passage C

percentile   grams   centimetres   centimetres

Four-month-old Michael Cheng has just had a routine child health check. He weighed 7200 (1)_____, measured 63 (2) _____ in length and his head circumference was 41 (3) _____. He is in the 90th (4) _____ for weight for a male baby of four months.

Passage D

puffs   days   day

Sue Mancini has acute sinusitis and an upper respiratory infection. Drug S has been prescribed for ten (1) _____. She needs to take one tablet twice a (2)_____ with food until all finished. In addition, she needs two (3)_____ per nostril each day of nasal spray N to help relieve her symptoms.

Passage E

beats   millimetres   weeks

Ultrasound findings: There is an intrauterine gestational sac with visible embryo, having a crown rump length of six (1)_____ . The heart rate is 124 (2)_____ per minute.

Conclusion: Single viable embryo with crown rump length in keeping with a gestational age of six (3)_____ two days.

Passage F

millilitres	times	dose	seconds

Mishka Kumar has asthma and bronchitis. She has been prescribed three (1)_____ of drug S in suspension once a day for three days only, to be taken with food. Please also ensure she uses a spacer with her inhaler. Press the inhaler once to release a single (2)_____ of the medicine into the spacer. She should breathe in slowly and hold her breath for a few (3)_____ before breathing out slowly through her mouth. Repeat four or five (4)_____ before administering the second dose.

Passage G

roll	sachets	packet	tube	vials

There is a (1)_____ of plasters, a (2)_____ of tape, several (3)_____ of antibacterial cleansing wipes, a (4)_____ of burn gel and several (5)_____ of sterile water in the first aid kit.

Passage H

hourly	times	centimetre	days

Apply a one (1)_____ ribbon of the eye ointment to the inside lower conjunctival sac five (2)_____ a day at approximately four (3)_____ intervals. Treatment should continue for fourteen (4)_____ or at least three days after healing is complete, whichever is shorter.

Passage I

hours	millilitres	year	times	kilograms

A five- (1) _____ -old child who weighs eighteen (2)_____ can take six (3)_____ of drug F every four to six (4)_____, if required, to a maximum of four (5)_____ in 24 hours.

Passage J

minutes	drops	days	

For the removal of ear wax: Approximately five (1)_____ should be instilled into the affected ear. Leave for ten to thirty (2)_____ and no longer than one hour. Repeat twice a day up to three (3) _____.

Passage K

To make formula for a baby aged between three and six (1)_____: Place three level (2)_____ of powder in 180 (3)_____ of cooled, boiled water. Your baby needs five feeds per (4)_____.

Passage L

Add the entire contents of one (1)_____ of drug K in a jug with 250 (2)_____ of water. Drink the mixture completely over five to ten (3)_____.

SETTING: THE SANCTUARY AGED CARE FACILITY

Resident Mrs Robinson was injured while using the lift at the Sanctuary Aged Care Facility. Read the following excerpt from the Incident Report. Notice the *verb forms* in bold.

Description of Incident

Mrs Gillian Robinson **states** that she **pushed** her wheelie walker into the lift as the lift doors **were closing** at around 1330. She **caught** her left hand (top) between the lift door and the wheelie walker. She **sustained** a skin tear to the top of her left hand and bruising. Another resident (Mrs Beryl Lucas), who **had witnessed** the incident, **notified** the nurse in charge.

Treatment

At 1400, the nurse in charge **treated** the skin tear with antiseptic and sterile adhesive strips and **applied** a cool pack to the bruising.

Report by Workplace Health and Safety Officer

A mandatory inspection of the lift was conducted following the incident. No failure of the lift doors was detected.

Future Recommendations

In future, a member of staff **will escort** Mrs Robinson in and out of the lift. The Director of Nursing **is considering** relocating Mrs Robinson to a ground floor room, closer to amenities, and **will consult** with her family.

GRAMMAR BOOST 1: TALKING ABOUT THE PAST

We use **past simple** to talk about:

A   a single action in the past that occurred at a specific time
   *Yesterday morning we **inserted** a nasogastric tube to assist with rehydration.*

B   multiple past actions which happened sequentially
   *Oliver Peters **fell** off his skateboard, **injured** his arm and **went** to hospital.*

We use **past continuous** to talk about:

C a continuous past action which was interrupted and has now finished
   *Mr Strong **was playing** tennis when he injured his shoulder.*

D two continuous past actions which occurred at the same time and have now finished
   *My son **was having** difficulty breathing while he **was running** around this afternoon.*

We use **present perfect** to talk about:

E past events which are connected to the present, which occurred at a non-specific time in the past
   *I **have** never **had** shingles.*
   *The doctor **has prescribed** non-opiate medications for pain relief.*

We use **present perfect continuous** to talk about:

F a continuous or repeated action which started in the past and continued until the time of speaking
   ***Have** you **been changing** the dressing every day?*

We use **past perfect** to talk about:

G an earlier past action which occurred before another past action
   *The general practitioner referred him to a specialist because his symptoms **had** not **resolved**.*

We use **past perfect continuous** to talk about:

H a continuous or repeated action that began in the past and finished in the past
   *Because he **had** not **been eating** enough fibre, he became constipated.*

PRACTICE 1: MATCHING FUNCTIONS OF VERB TENSES 1

Choose the most suitable explanation (A-H) from Grammar Boost 1 to describe the use of the verb tense (in *italics*) in each sentence. An example (0) has been done for you.

0 Mr White *absconded* during the morning. **(A)**

1 When the ambulance arrived, a passer-by *had started* cardiac pulmonary resuscitation (CPR). (   )

2 *Have* you *noticed* any pain in your hip previously? (   )

3 The nurse *was withdrawing* the needle when the resident moved. (   )

4 Mr Shaw *had not been using* his inhaler correctly so the pharmacy assistant showed him how to use a spacer. (   )

5 *Have* you *been having* trouble sleeping? (   )

6 Omar's dog *bit* him, his mother *took* him to the clinic and he *needed* a tetanus booster shot. (   )

7 The baby *was sleeping* while the audiologist *was conducting* a hearing test. (   )

GRAMMAR BOOST 2: TALKING ABOUT THE PRESENT

We use **present simple** to talk about:

A   a habit or routine
   *Mr Perez always **takes** his tablets crushed and mixed with yoghurt.*

B   a scientific fact/a general truth
   *The left side of the brain **controls** the right side of the body.*
   *Children with croup **do not** usually **require** supplementary oxygen.*

C   permanent or long lasting situations
   *I **live** in Auckland where I **work** as a plastic surgeon.*

D   timetables or schedules
   *Visiting hours **finish** at 8pm.*

We use **present continuous** to talk about:

E   an action in progress at the time of speaking
   *His new kidney **is functioning** perfectly.*

F   a repeated temporary action over a specific period of time
   *While Dr Faulkner is on annual leave, Dr Liddell **is seeing** all of the patients at the clinic.*

PRACTICE 2: MATCHING FUNCTIONS OF VERB TENSES 2

Choose the most suitable explanation (A-F) from Grammar Boost 2 to describe the use of the verb tense (in *italics*) in each sentence. An example (0) has been done for you.

0   The influenza vaccine is temporarily unavailable due to a supply shortage. The health department *is advising* high-risk patients to contact their general practitioner for further information. **(F)**

1   Cystic fibrosis primarily *affects* the respiratory, digestive and reproductive systems. (   )

2   I *operate* heavy machinery for a living. (   )

3   Dr Mackay *plays* golf on weekends. (   )

4   I *am escorting* Mrs Hayes to breakfast. I will be with you in a moment. (   )

5   Radiology services *commence* at 9am. (   )

GRAMMAR BOOST 3: TALKING ABOUT THE FUTURE

We use **will** to talk about:

A   a spontaneous response to a situation
   *He is losing consciousness. I **will call** the doctor.*

B   making a prediction
     *The surgery **will last** for about 3 hours.*

We use **present continuous** to talk about:

C   a definite future arrangement
     *You **are coming** in for a procedure next Tuesday. Is that correct?*

We use **going to** to talk about:

D   a definite intention or plan
     *We **are going to** start this drip at 10 millilitres per hour.*

We use **present simple with a time reference** to talk about:

E   timetables or schedules with a future meaning
     *The clinic **opens at 7am tomorrow**.*

We use **future continuous** to talk about:

F   an action in progress in the future
     *Hi. My name is Fiona. I **will be taking** care of you today.*

We use **future perfect** to talk about:

G   a completed action in the future
     *By this afternoon, we **will have removed** your urinary catheter and you will be able to resume toileting as normal.*

PRACTICE 3: MATCHING FUNCTIONS WITH VERB TENSES 3

Choose the most suitable explanation (A-G) from Grammar Boost 3 to describe the use of the verb tense (in italics) in each sentence. An example (0) has been done for you.

0   Baby Olsen **is having** a frenectomy tomorrow morning. **(C)**

1   We are sending Mrs Zhang to hospital now. **Will** you **contact** her next of kin? (   )

2   The results of the blood test **will confirm** the diagnosis. (   )

3   The physiotherapist **is going to** teach you how to get out of bed after surgery. (   )

4   You **will be staying** in respite care for 5 days. (   )

5   By the time my shift ends, I **will have updated** all the care plans. (   )

6   Dr Walker **starts** her rounds at 1530 this afternoon. (   )

GRAMMAR BOOST 4: FOR, SINCE AND AGO

For + a period of time can be used to talk about duration of actions in the past, present and future.

*Give 2 millilitres of fluid orally every 2 minutes **for three hours**.*

*Mr Dawson has had a productive cough **for almost a week**.*

*The radiation therapy will last **for 35 days**.*

*My daughter has had a temperature of more than 38.5°C **for 4 days**.*

*This morning I lost vision in my left eye **for about 10 minutes**.*

Since + a specific point of time in the past can be used with the present perfect simple and continuous and the past perfect simple and continuous.

*Mr Kapoor has not passed urine **since the surgery.***

*How have you been feeling **since you finished the course of antibiotics?***

*Mr Cheng has been experiencing severe headaches **since Tuesday**.*

*She has vomited 7 times **since 2pm**.*

*His wife said he had been on the waiting list for surgery **since March last year**.*

***Since he started the medication**, his condition had been improving, but it suddenly deteriorated.*

*Carl Jensen has had a colostomy bag **since October 6**.*

A time phrase + ago can be used to talk about how long before the moment of speaking a single action was completed. *Ago* is most commonly used with the past simple not the present perfect.

*Luke Forsythe suffered a minor head injury **a month ago**.*

*She sustained a severe laceration to her face in an accident **a week ago**.*

*I spoke to Jasmine King's parents **10 minutes ago**.*

*Amir Malik had a tonsillectomy and adenoidectomy about **25 years ago**.*

PRACTICE 4: ERROR CORRECTION

Look carefully at each line in the following texts. Some of the lines are correct and some contain one extra word which should not be there. If a line is correct, put a tick (✔) in the space provided at the end of the line. If a line has an extra word that should not be there, write the word in the space provided at the end of the line. Two examples have been done for you, (00) and (0).

00	Your husband ~~has~~ came to hospital with tightness in his chest about an hour ago. The	**has**
0	nurse is taking observations at 5 minute intervals. The doctor saw him on arrival and	✔
1	will be reviewing his condition in a few minutes. You will be able to see him soon.	

2	Eight-year-old Matthew Yang has jumped out of a tree at about 4 o'clock this
3	afternoon. His mother believes that he did hit the left side of his head. He briefly lost
4	consciousness. By the time he reached hospital he had vomited twice. He is now being
5	in hospital under observation and will undergo a series of scans shortly.

6	Mrs Lawson is been in the first stage of labour. She has been in labour for 36 hours.
7	She is 3 centimetres dilated. The baby is showing signs of distress. The obstetrician has
8	had decided that Mrs Lawson will have an emergency caesarean section. She is going to go to theatre now.

9	Louisa Bradshaw was cooking dinner when she picked up a hot pan and burned her
10	hand. She was immersed it in cool water for about an hour and then came to hospital
11	It is a superficial burn which will need a dressing. She does not to require hospitalisation.

12	You have a serious eye infection called ocular herpes. It is be a recurrent viral infection
13	which will affects the eyes. It is contagious so you will need to avoid close contact with
14	others until treatment has finished. I will to give you a prescription for an eye
15	ointment. You need to apply it every 4 hours. The chemist will show you exactly what to do.

PRACTICE 5: SENTENCE TRANSFORMATION

Complete the second sentence so that it has a similar meaning to the first sentence. Use the word in bold. Do not change the word in bold. Use between 2 and 5 words including the word in bold. An example (0) has been done for you.

0   not

She last saw the oncologist 2 months ago.

She has _____ **not seen the oncologist for** _____ 2 months.

1   going

The doctor intends to make a small incision to remove your splinter.

The doctor _____ a small incision to remove your splinter.

2   while

Jack Nichols sustained a groin strain during a game of hockey.

Jack Nichols sustained a groin strain _____ hockey.

3   been

Amber Ling began taking this medication 6 weeks ago.

Amber Ling has _____ 6 weeks.

4   long

When did you start using your inhaler without a spacer?

_____ using your inhaler without a spacer?

5   not

It is the first time she has had a febrile seizure.

She _____ a febrile seizure before.

6   had

A venous blood clot formed in her right lower leg so she was referred to a vascular surgeon.

She was referred to a vascular surgeon because a_____
in her right lower leg.

7   had

The family went home before the social worker arrived.

When the social worker_____ home.

8 **to**

Quick! She is about to faint.

Quick! She _____ faint.

9 **fall**

Felicity Singh fell at 11.45 this morning and fractured her femur.

Felicity Singh _____ at 11.45 this morning and fractured her femur.

10 **at**

The clinic's closing time is 1pm on Saturdays.

The clinic _____ 1pm on Saturdays.

PRACTICE 6: MULTIPLE CHOICE CLOZE

Read the following Letters of Referral. Choose the most suitable answer A, B or C to complete each sentence with the correct verb form. An example (0) has been done for you.

Letter 1

Dear Trevor

Thank you for seeing Mr Drew McDonald, aged 47 years, whom I **(0) <u>consulted</u>** today. Drew (1) _____ his left hand 9 days ago and (2) _____ bilateral hand pain. I enclose Drew's ultrasound report which suggests collateral ligament rupture of his Metacarpophalangeal joint - left thumb, however ultrasound and x-ray were inconclusive. The ultrasound (3) _____ a possible small avulsion fracture fragment, however this is not clearly identified on the x-ray. Therefore, I (4) _____ magnetic resonance imaging (MRI) for further assessment, which Drew (5) _____ prior to seeing you. I reprint for your information, my history, examination and investigation findings together with relevant Past History, Allergies, Current Medications and Investigation Results.

Thank you for your care and assistance.

Yours sincerely
Dr Brian Smith

0	**A** <u>consulted</u>	**B** have consulted	**C** had consulted
1	**A** has injured	**B** had injured	**C** injured
2	**A** experiences	**B** is experiencing	**C** will experience
3	**A** detects	**B** detected	**C** had detected
4	**A** have ordered	**B** have been ordering	**C** have not ordered
5	**A** does	**B** going to do	**C** will have done

Letter 2

Dear Ricardo

Thank you for seeing Camilla Fernandez, aged 8 years, for chronic abdominal pain with intermittent diarrhoea which (1) _____ ongoing since a severe episode of gastroenteritis 4-5 months ago. She (2) _____ weight, but has missed a good amount of school this term related to fatigue, sore tummy and recurrent abdominal pain. Stool tests are enclosed with dientamoeba being the only positive consistent finding. She (3) _____ but recently plateaued. I (4) _____ blood tests including coeliac serology and fecal calprotectin. I (5)_____ the results to you when they become available.

Yours sincerely

Dr Maria Varela

1	**A** was	**B** been	**C** has been
2	**A** have not lost	**B** has not lost	**C** did not lost
3	**A** is improving	**B** improves	**C** had been improving
4	**A** had organised	**B** have organised	**C** have been organising
5	**A** will forward	**B** am forwarding	**C** forward

UNIT 6 | PASSIVES

SETTING: CITY CHILDREN'S HOSPITAL

Nurse Paul Ramos has just finished his shift at City Children's Hospital. He is giving an update to nurses on the next shift. His account of a young patient is written below. Notice the *passive structures* in bold.

> Miss Lola Wilson, aged 3, **was admitted** yesterday morning with a recent history of lethargy, frequent urination and excessive thirst. She **was examined** yesterday and initial tests **have been conducted**. Further investigations are ongoing. A probable diagnosis is Type 1 diabetes. She **is being monitored** very closely. Her condition **will be reviewed** this morning by a specialist. Her parents **need to be shown** how to check her blood sugar levels and how to administer insulin. Upon discharge, a community nurse **will be assigned** to the family for 2 weeks to assist Mr and Mrs Wilson to monitor Miss Wilson's blood sugar levels and give insulin, as well as to offer support.

GRAMMAR BOOST 1: PASSIVES – WHEN TO USE PASSIVES

WE USE THE PASSIVE WHEN:	ACTIVE	PASSIVE
we want to focus on the object of the sentence.	*An endocrinologist will review **her condition** this morning.*	*Her condition will be reviewed this morning.*
the agent is clear.	***Medical staff** are monitoring her very closely.*	*She is being monitored very closely.*
the agent is unknown.	***Somebody** needs to show her parents how to check her blood sugar levels.*	*Her parents need to be shown how to check her blood sugar levels.*
the agent is unimportant.	***Hospital staff** admitted Lola Wilson yesterday with a recent history of lethargy, frequent urination and excessive thirst.*	*Lola Wilson was admitted yesterday with a recent history of lethargy, frequent urination and excessive thirst.*

BOOSTER TIP - AGENT OR NO AGENT?

1 Sometimes it is necessary to mention who does the action. If we want to mention the agent, we use **by.**

*Her condition will be reviewed this morning **by** a specialist.*

2 The passive is useful to express rules and guidelines which apply to everybody. It is not necessary to mention an agent.

Payment is requested at the time of your appointment.

No jewellery is to be worn.

All valuables are to be left at home.

3 The passive is often used with the reporting verbs *say, believe, know, understand.*

He is said to be *one of the best endocrinologists in town.*

OR

It is said that *he is one of the best endocrinologists in town.*

She is known to be *the leading burns specialist in the country.*

OR

It is known that *she is the leading burns specialist in the country.*

4 To be born is a form of passive. There is no active form.

*The baby **was born** at 5.16pm yesterday.*

GRAMMAR BOOST 2: PASSIVES – HOW TO FORM PASSIVES

TENSE	STRUCTURE	EXAMPLE
present simple	am/are/is + past participle	*Antibiotics are not prescribed for viral infections.*
present continuous	am/are/is being + past participle	*The patient is being stabilised prior to surgery.*
past simple	was/were + past participle	*She was sent to the Emergency Department by her general practitioner.*
past continuous	was/were being + past participle	*The patients were being treated when their relatives arrived.*
present perfect	have/has been + past participle	*Have her relatives been informed?*
past perfect	had been + past participle	*He was disappointed that he had not been selected for the clinical trial.*
future with *will*	will be + past participle	*The baby will be delivered by caesarean section tomorrow.*
future with *going to*	am/are/is going to be + past participle	*You are not going to be rostered on for night duty next week.*
modal verbs	modal verb + be + past participle	*The paper work must be completed prior to admission.*

BOOSTER TIP - TRANSITIVE VERBS WITH PASSIVE FORMS

1 Only transitive verbs (verbs followed by a direct object) can be used in a passive form.

They faxed the referral to the specialist. (active)   *The referral was faxed to the specialist (passive)*

2 Most transitive verbs can be made passive, however some transitive verbs do not have a passive form. *(e.g. become, fit, get, have, lack, let, like, resemble, suit)*

3 Verbs with two objects can be used in the passive in different ways.

ACTIVE: *The doctor gave him a prescription.*

PASSIVE: *He was given a prescription. OR A prescription was given to him.*

GRAMMAR BOOST 3: CAUSATIVES - WHEN TO USE CAUSATIVES

When someone performs a service for us, or we organise for someone (often a professional or specialist) to do something for us, we use have something done. It is sometimes called *causative*.

*Mrs Sheehy **has her blood sugar levels checked** 3 times per day.*

Needs doing is used when some kind of action is required. It is informal.

These beds need making.

This commode needs emptying.

GRAMMAR BOOST 4: CAUSATIVES- HOW TO FORM CAUSATIVES

TENSE	STRUCTURE	EXAMPLE
present simple	have/has + something + past participle	Mrs Davies has her dressing changed daily by the community nurse.
present continuous	am/are/is having + something + past participle	He is having his eyes tested at the moment.
past simple	had + something + past participle	She had an ovarian cyst removed last June.
past continuous	was/were having + something + past participle	Mr Vescovi was having blood taken when he fainted.
present perfect	have/has had + something + past participle	Has your daughter ever had her teeth checked by a dentist?
past perfect	had had + something + past participle	He had had his breathing monitored at the sleep clinic and was later diagnosed with sleep apnoea.
future with will	will have + something + past participle	Mrs Parker will have her ears syringed in a few moments.
future with going to	am/are/is going to + have + something + past participle	Mrs Fong is going to have a cardiac pacemaker implanted on Thursday.
modal verbs	modal verb + have + something + past participle	She can have her husband collected for day respite if she is unable to drive.

PRACTICE 1: COMPLETE THE SENTENCE

Read the following staff memo. Complete each sentence with the most suitable option (A-H) from the box. An example (0) has been done for you.

A	has been misplaced	**E**	need reminding
B	are to be taken	**F**	**will be inducted**
C	were cancelled	**G**	have been rescheduled
D	have their teeth checked	**H**	will no longer be served

ST PETER'S NURSING HOME

From: Director of Nursing

To: All staff

Re: Weekly memo

New staff Induction

New staff **(0) will be inducted** on Thursday at 9.00am.

Infection Control Workshops

The infection control workshops (1) _____ last week due to unforeseen circumstances. They (2) _____ and will now be held every day next week prior to the start of each shift. Please arrive 30 minutes before your shift as the workshops will start on time. All workshops will be led by the infection control consultant and will be supported by the registered nurse on duty.

Lost property cupboard

The key to the lost property cupboard (3) _____. Please check your pockets!

Meals in Rooms

For health and safety reasons, meals (4) _____ in residents' rooms unless the resident is ill or incapacitated. Meals (5)_____ in the dining room. Residents have been informed about this but may (6) _____.

Dental appointments

Visiting dentist, Dr Charles Wong, will see patients at St Peter's every day next week. Residents can make an appointment to (7) _____ between 9am and 12pm. Dr Wong's services will be bulk billed.

PRACTICE 2: ERROR CORRECTION

Read the following questions and sentences. Some are correct and some contain one extra word which should not be there. For each sentence or question, put a tick (✔) if it is correct. If it is incorrect write the extra word in the space provided at the end of the line. Two examples, (00) and (0), have been done for you.

00	Mrs Santos ~~was~~ required assistance to walk while in hospital.	was
0	Mr Wallin was diagnosed with non-insulin dependent diabetes mellitus in 2000.	✔
1	Is Mr Finnigan being discharged this morning?	
2	Mrs Garcia was presented to the Emergency Department last night with breathing difficulties.	
3	Mr Cox will be referred to a dietician as he has been gained a lot of weight recently.	
4	Adrenalin was administered following an allergic reaction.	
5	A specialist will be consulted regarding the diagnosis.	
6	Mr Donald's condition has been deteriorated.	
7	Her blood pressure is be closely monitored by her general practitioner.	
8	Further testing will be conducted over the next few days.	
9	You will be examined as soon as a doctor becomes available.	
10	Miss Simpson has been contracted chickenpox.	
11	Had Mrs Elliott been diagnosed with a urinary tract infection before she was admitted to hospital?	
12	Mr Mackay has not been had his wound checked this afternoon.	

PRACTICE 3: COMPLETE THE SENTENCE

Change the following active sentences into passive or causative forms. Do not change the tense. Use between 2 and 5 words. An example (0) has been done for you.

0   You **must take** these pills with food.

These pills ***must be taken*** with food.

1   The doctor **discharged** Mr Kapoor this morning.

Mr Kapoor _____ this morning.

2   How often do I **need to change** this dressing?

How often does_____ changed?

3   Screws and a metal plate **will hold** the new bone in place.

The new bone _____in place with screws and a metal plate.

4   The nurse **has not given** Millie Goodwin any pain relief yet.

Millie Goodwin _____ any pain relief yet.

5   A plastic surgeon **is going to remove** the skin cancer on his ear tomorrow.

The skin cancer on his ear _____ by a plastic surgeon tomorrow.

6   The doctor **has diagnosed** Mr Douglas with kidney stones.

Mr Douglas _____ kidney stones.

7   **Has** anyone **ordered** Mr Almeida's inhalers from the pharmacy yet?

_____ Mr Almeida's inhalers _____ from the pharmacy yet?

8   **Has** a dermatologist ever **checked** your skin?

Have you ever _____ your skin _____a dermatologist?

9   Nobody **had cleaned** the wound properly and an infection developed.

The wound _____and an infection developed.

10 They **admitted** Ms Lee to hospital with acute abdominal pain.

Ms Lee _____ acute abdominal pain.

11 Medical experts **recommend** that people have a tetanus booster shot every ten years.

It _____ people have a tetanus booster shot every ten years.

12 Please wait here, Mr Kennedy. The doctor **is treating** Mrs Kennedy for shock and minor cuts and abrasions.

Please wait here, Mr Kennedy. Mrs Kennedy _____
for shock and minor cuts and abrasions.

PRACTICE 4: MULTIPLE CHOICE CLOZE

Read the following Letter of Discharge. Choose the most suitable answer A, B or C to complete each sentence. An example (0) has been done for you.

Ms Christine Mason
Nurse in Charge
Low Isles Retirement Home
4 Beet Street, Newland

4 September (year)

Dear Ms Mason

Re: Mrs Catherine Hamilton (aged 70)

Mrs Hamilton **(0) is being discharged** from Royal Hospital back into your care today. Mrs Hamilton (1) _____ on 30 August (insert year) having suffered a myocardial infarction.

Mrs Hamilton (2) _____ with shortness of breath, discomfort in her chest and pain in both arms. Supplemental oxygen (3) _____ upon arrival at hospital. The medical officer prescribed pain relief. She was transferred to the Coronary Care Unit and monitored (4) _____ the resident cardiologist. She was confined to bed rest for 24 hours.

Initially, Mrs Hamilton (5) _____ assistance with all activities of daily living. She is now able to walk unassisted and can shower and use the toilet with minimal assistance. She can walk up a single flight of stairs with supervision. She should ambulate regularly and continue to participate in light exercise.

Mrs Hamilton (6) _____ to the outpatient cardiac clinic at Royal Hospital for rehabilitation. Appointment dates for the cardiac rehabilitation programme (7)_____ to Mrs Hamilton by the end of this week. In addition, cardiac patients (8) _____ to attend the cardiac support group meetings which (9) _____ weekly at the outpatient cardiac clinic.

Mrs Hamilton (10) _____ a follow-up appointment at Royal Hospital at 10am on 27 September (year).

Please contact me if you have any queries.

Yours sincerely
Nurse in Charge
Royal Hospital

0	**A** is discharging	**B** was being discharged	**C** <u>**is being discharged**</u>
1	**A** has been admitted	**B** was admitted	**C** is admitted
2	**A** has been presented	**B** was presented	**C** presented
3	**A** was administered	**B** is being administered	**C** administered
4	**A** for	**B** by	**C** with
5	**A** was required	**B** required	**C** is required
6	**A** has been referred	**B** has referred	**C** have been referred
7	**A** be sent	**B** will be sent	**C** will send
8	**A** are encouraging	**B** should encourage	**C** are encouraged
9	**A** are held	**B** held	**C** is held
10	**A** has been made	**B** was made	**C** has

UNIT 7 | CONDITIONALS

SETTING: SHERIDAN CITY HIGH SCHOOL

A school nurse recently spoke to a group of teenagers about the importance of maintaining a healthy body weight. Read the following summary of the talk. Notice the *conditional forms* in bold.

- Maintaining a healthy weight throughout adolescence may reduce the risk of becoming overweight or obese as an adult. Being overweight or underweight can negatively affect your health. In particular, being overweight or obese can result in serious health problems.

- **Provided that** you eat balanced, healthy meals and get regular exercise, your weight should stay within an acceptable range. Participating in physical activity every day of the week is integral to maintaining a healthy weight.

- **If** you are overweight, ask your doctor for advice on the best way to lose weight.

- Do not follow a very low calorie diet **unless** it is recommended by your doctor. Diets which are extremely low in calories can have serious side effects.

- **If** you are underweight, please see your doctor **in case** there is an underlying medical problem which is affecting your weight.

GRAMMAR BOOST 1: CONDITIONAL FORMS 1

Zero conditional

- **Always true**

*If you **exercise** regularly, your level of fitness **increases**.*

First conditional

- **Talking about real situations**

***Will** I **lose** weight **if** I **reduce** my calorie intake?*

***If** it **rains** this afternoon, school sport **will be cancelled**.*

*He **might** join the local football team **if** they **are accepting** new members.*

Second conditional

- **Talking about imaginary or unreal situations**

***If** you **ate** healthy meals and **exercised** regularly, you **would** probably **lose** weight.*

Third conditional

- **Talking about imaginary or unreal past events**

***If** I **had exercised** regularly over the last 12 months, I **would not have gained** so much weight.*

Mixed conditional

- Talking about imaginary or unreal past events with a present result

*If I **had eaten** more healthily when I was a teenager, I **would not be** overweight now.*

GRAMMAR BOOST 2: CONDITIONAL FORMS 2

- **provided that / as long as** means *only if*

***Provided (that) / As long as** you eat balanced, healthy meals and get regular exercise, your weight should stay within an acceptable range.*

- **in case** means to be prepared for the *possibility* that....

*If you are underweight, please see your doctor **in case** there is an underlying problem which is affecting your weight.*

- **unless** means *if...not*

*Do not follow a very low calorie diet **unless** it is recommended by your doctor.*

GRAMMAR BOOST 3: WISHES AND REGRETS

- **wish + would** is used to express a desire for change in someone's behaviour.

*I **wish** you **would** talk to a doctor about your cough. You have had it for 3 weeks.*

- **wish + simple past** is used to express a desire to change a present or future state.

*I **wish** I **had** more time to exercise.*

- **wish + had + past participle** is used to express a regret about past events which cannot be changed.

*I **wish** I **had attended** the school nurse's talk last week. People said it was very interesting.*

PRACTICE 1: MATCHING CONDITIONAL SENTENCES WITH THEIR MEANING

Read the conditional sentences in bold. Tick the TWO sentences (A, B, C or D) which best match the meaning of the sentence given in bold. An example (0) has been done for you.

0   If I had not fallen down the stairs, I would not have broken my leg.

A	I did not fall down the stairs.	
B	<u>I fell down the stairs.</u>	✔
C	I did not break my leg.	
D	<u>I broke my leg.</u>	✔

1 **Mrs Blythe wishes she did not need daily hormone injections.**

A	Mrs Blythe needs daily hormone injections.	
B	Mrs Blythe does not need daily hormone injections.	
C	Mrs Blythe is happy about having daily hormone injections.	
D	Mrs Blythe is not happy about having daily hormone injections.	

2 **If you had some domestic support, you would be able to remain in your own home.**

A	You have domestic support.	
B	You do not have domestic support.	
C	Without domestic support, you can remain in your own home.	
D	Without domestic support, you cannot remain in your own home.	

3 **If Mrs Callea had not had a PET (Positron Emission Tomography) scan, the tumour might not have been discovered until much later.**

A	Mrs Callea had a PET scan.	
B	Mrs Callea did not have a PET scan.	
C	A tumour was discovered.	
D	A tumour was not discovered.	

4 **I wish I had not taken my son to the Emergency Department last night. He only has a cold!**

A	I took my son to the Emergency Department last night.	
B	I did not take my son to the Emergency Department last night.	
C	I regret taking my son to the Emergency Department last night.	
D	I do not regret taking my son to the Emergency Department last night.	

5 **If my tooth had not been removed, the dentist said it would have become infected.**

A	My tooth was removed.	
B	My tooth was not removed.	
C	My tooth became infected.	
D	My tooth did not become infected.	

6 **If you had taken the medication with food as directed, you would not feel nauseous now.**

A	You took the medication with food.
B	You did not take the medication with food.
C	You feel nauseous now.
D	You do not feel nauseous now.

7 **I wish he would stop smoking. He has terrible emphysema.**

A	He has stopped smoking.
B	He has not stopped smoking.
C	The speaker would like him to stop smoking.
D	The speaker would not like him to stop smoking.

PRACTICE 2: SENTENCE COMPLETION

Choose the most suitable answer A, B or C to complete the sentences. An example (0) has been done for you.

0 Here is a bag

    A   **in case you vomit.**

    B   unless you vomit.

    C   as long you vomit.

1 If you need a nurse,

    A   will press this button.

    B   press this button.

    C   should press this button.

2 If I were you,

    A   I would call a doctor.

    B   I will call a doctor.

    C   I have called a doctor.

3 She can continue taking the drug

    A   in case it causes an adverse reaction.

    B   unless it causes an adverse reaction.

    C   if it causes an adverse reaction.

4   You will be able to manage your diabetes

    A   provided you monitor your blood sugar levels and take your medication as discussed.

    B   in case you monitor your blood sugar levels and take your medication as discussed.

    C   unless you monitor your blood sugar levels and take your medication as discussed.

5   The physiotherapist says unless you exercise your leg daily

    A   it will not become stiff.

    B   in case it becomes stiff.

    C   it will become stiff.

6   There is no need to make another appointment

    A   as long as her condition deteriorates.

    B   unless her condition deteriorates.

    C   provided that her condition deteriorates.

7   All family members should know where the asthma medication is kept

    A   in case she has an attack.

    B   unless she has an attack.

    C   provided that she has an attack.

8   Notify the blood collector

    A   provided that you are allergic to medical tapes or lotions.

    B   as long as you are allergic to medical tapes or lotions.

    C   if you are allergic to medical tapes or lotions.

9   You will be required to stay at the blood collection centre until you fully recover

    A   unless you faint again.

    B   if you faint again.

    C   provided that you faint again.

PRACTICE 3: SENTENCE COMPLETION

Match the beginning of sentences in Column A with the most suitable ending in Column B. Write your answers in the space provided. An example (0) has been done for you.

COLUMN A	COLUMN B
0 <u>Pack a bag for her to take to hospital</u>	A if you continue to have problems with your eyesight.
1 Ask the doctor if	B <u>**in case she is admitted.**</u>
2 Provided that there are no complications during surgery	C unless it is an emergency.
3 You should not call an ambulance	D Mrs Duncan's test results have been received.
4 Ice packs should help to reduce the swelling	E bring the films to the appointment with the specialist.
5 You will need to see an ophthalmologist	F you should be able to have visitors soon after you return to the ward.
6 If you have had any scans or x-rays	G if you have sprained your ankle.

Write your answers here.

0	1	2	3	4	5	6
B						

PRACTICE 4: COMPLETE THE SENTENCE

SETTING: SUBURBAN MEDICAL CLINIC

A patient has had a leg wound dressed at the clinic. The patient is asking the nurse for advice about caring for the wound at home.

Choose the most suitable word from the box to complete each of the following sentences. You may need to use an expression more than once. An example (0) has been done for you.

in case   if   provided (that)   as long as   unless

0   Patient: How long will this dressing last?

    Nurse: It should last for about four days <u>**unless**</u> the wound becomes infected.

1   Patient: What signs of infection should I look for?

    Nurse: _____ you notice tenderness, redness or oozing at the wound site, you might have an infection.

2   Patient: Can I have a shower with the dressing on?

      Nurse: Yes, showering is recommended _____ you keep the dressing dry.

3   Patient: How can I keep the dressing dry?

      Nurse: Cover it in plastic while you are in the shower. It should stay dry _____ it is fully covered.

4   Patient: What should I do if the dressing gets wet?

      Nurse: I will give you a spare dressing _____ this one gets wet. You will be able to change it yourself.

5   Patient: When should I come back to see the doctor?

      Nurse: _____ there are no signs of infection, you should not need to see the doctor until next week.

PRACTICE 5: SENTENCE TRANSFORMATION

Complete the second sentence so that it has a similar meaning to the first sentence. Use the word in bold. Do not change the word in bold. Use between 2 and 5 words including the word in bold. An example (0) has been done for you.

0   wishes

Mrs Fielding cannot remember simple things. She would like to be able to.

Mrs Fielding _____ **wishes she could remember** _____ simple things.

1   case

Do not get out of bed without assistance because there is a risk of falling.

Do not get out of bed without assistance _____ a fall.

2   if

I did not ask the doctor for a new prescription and I ran out of medication.

I would not have run out of medication _____ the doctor for a new prescription.

3   unless

Use this inhaler only when you are feeling breathless.

Do _____ you are feeling breathless.

4   if

Mr Patel is in hospital because he broke his hip.

Mr Patel would_____ he had not broken his hip.

5 **wish**

I regret taking that supplement without asking for the doctor's advice. I feel terrible!

I _____ that supplement without asking for the doctor's advice. I feel terrible!

6 **unless**

If you do not protect yourself against the sun, your skin will burn.

Your skin will burn _____ yourself against the sun.

7 **long**

You can stay in your own home provided that you have daily visits from a nurse.

You can stay in your own home _____ daily visits from a nurse.

8 **if**

Your recovery is slow because you do not do your exercises every day.

Your recovery would be faster _____ every day.

9 **provided**

If her condition deteriorates, we will not be able to operate this afternoon.

We will be able to operate this afternoon _____ deteriorate.

10 **case**

I will give you a repeat for this prescription. Your infection might need further treatment.

I will give you a repeat for this prescription _____ needs further treatment.

SETTING: BEDFORD VILLAGE COMMUNITY CENTRE

Bedford Village Community Centre is holding an information session on food allergies and intolerances. Read the following advertisement for the session. Notice the *prepositions* used after the adjectives and verbs in bold.

Food intolerance and allergy information session

with an accredited practising dietician

Do you **suffer from** abdominal pain, nausea, distension, diarrhoea or constipation?

Do you get hives or rashes?

Food allergies or food intolerances may be the cause.

If you are **interested in learning** more **about** food allergies and intolerances, come to our informative session where an accredited practising dietician will **talk about:**

- signs and symptoms **associated with** food allergies and food intolerances
- why your body may **react to** certain foods
- allergy testing **based on** the latest research
- elimination diets and whether they are **suitable for** you
- avoiding allergens and known triggers without compromising your health

Wednesday, 10.00am, at the community centre

GRAMMAR BOOST 1: DEPENDENT PREPOSITIONS

Certain adjectives and verbs are commonly followed by a specific preposition before the object of the verb. These prepositions are called dependent prepositions and are followed by a noun (or pronoun) or verb in the -ing form (also called a gerund).

Adjective + preposition + noun/pronoun

*A dietician will talk about elimination diets and whether they are **suitable for you**.*

Adjective + preposition + verb+ing

*If you are **interested in learning** more about food allergies and intolerances, come to our informative session.*

Verb + preposition + noun/pronoun

Do you **suffer from abdominal pain?**

Verb + preposition + verb+ing

A dietician will **talk about avoiding** allergens without compromising your health.

GRAMMAR BOOST 2: ADJECTIVES + PREPOSITIONS

Examples of adjective + preposition combinations

adjective + of afraid, aware, capable, full, indicative, scared, short, suspicious, tired, typical, wary	• Following the surgery he will be **incapable of** showering independently for a week. • Mr Camilleri's symptoms are **indicative of** a bacterial infection so we will have to do some tests. • Mr Schmidt is **short of** breath. • What side effects are **typical of** this medication?
adjective + about angry, annoyed, anxious, certain, compassionate, concerned, embarrassed, nervous, pleased, positive, serious, upset, worried	• I understand you are **annoyed about** having to stay overnight in hospital, but we need to keep you here for observation. • Is Mr Smith **anxious about** being moved to another room? • I am **concerned about** her blood sugar levels. We need to investigate further. • Understandably, she is **upset about** the diagnosis.
adjective + in deficient, experienced, high, interested, low, rich	• The test results indicate that you are **deficient in** vitamin B12. You will need to take a supplement. • The neurosurgeon is very **experienced in** paediatric care. • He is not **interested in** participating in the clinical trial.

adjective + for	
early, eligible, grateful, late, necessary, ready, responsible, suitable	<ul><li>*Am I **eligible for** in-home respite care?*</li><li>*Dr Thomas said Mrs Wong is **ready for** discharge.*</li><li>*Who is **responsible for** keeping this care plan up to date?*</li></ul>
adjective + to	
accustomed, addicted, allergic, beneficial, detrimental, immune, opposed, prone, receptive, relevant, similar, susceptible, vulnerable	<ul><li>*With practice, you will become **accustomed to** administering insulin yourself.*</li><li>*Mr Tanaka is **allergic to** penicillin.*</li><li>*If you have already had the virus, you are **immune to** it.*</li><li>*New mothers who have difficulty breastfeeding may be **prone to** postpartum depression.*</li><li>*Immunosuppressed cancer patients are particularly **susceptible** to infection.*</li></ul>
adjective + with	
angry, annoyed, compatible, familiar, frustrated, pleased, satisfied, upset	<ul><li>*I understand you are **frustrated with** me, but I cannot give you any more pain relief without speaking to the doctor.*</li><li>*I am very **pleased with** the results of the surgery. You can hardly see the scar.*</li><li>*Were you **satisfied with** the care you received at the Emergency Department?*</li></ul>
adjective + on	
dependent, reliant	<ul><li>*Mrs Fielding is **dependent on** her walker or a wheelchair when she leaves her house.*</li></ul>
adjective + from	
different, safe	<ul><li>*This treatment is **different from** the last one so hopefully you will experience fewer side effects.*</li><li>*Medications in the home should be kept in a place that is **safe from** children.*</li></ul>

PRACTICE 1: MATCHING SENTENCE BEGINNINGS AND ENDINGS

Match the beginning of sentences in Column A with the most suitable ending in Column B.
Write your answers in the space provided. An example (0) has been done for you.

COLUMN A	COLUMN B
0 <u>Mr Smith is reliant</u>	A to foodborne illnesses.
1 Older adults, yong children and pregnant women are the most vulnerable	B with the disease.
2 Mrs Casey is short	C to your daughter's condition. Please read it.
3 Mrs Atkins is about to start chemotherapy and is anxious	D about losing her hair.
4 His unusual behaviour is associated	**E** <u>on his family for his day-to-day care.</u>
5 He is interested	F for surgical intervention.
6 This information is relevant	G from work for 4 days and I need a medical certificate.
7 I have been absent	H in learning more about his disease. Please give him this leaflet.
8 Unfortunately, it is too late	I of pills. I will call the pharmacy.

Write your answers here.

0	1	2	3	4	5	6	7	8
E								

PRACTICE 2: COMPLETE THE SENTENCE - ADJECTIVE + PREPOSITION

Complete each sentence with the most suitable preposition. An example (0) has been done for you.

0   Close medical supervision of patients is required to prevent them from becoming **dependent on** this drug.

1   It is easy for toddlers to become **deficient** _____ iron. You have to encourage them to eat a varied diet, including some meat.

2   If you are not **capable** _____ walking without assistance, I will organise a walker for you.

3   He will be **eligible** _____ outpatient physiotherapy after he is discharged from hospital.

4   If I have the influenza vaccine, will I be **immune** _____ all strains of the virus?

5   Ceasing the medication before you have taken the full course may be **detrimental** _____ your recovery.

6   His hair is **full** _____ lice. Please advise his mother of available treatments.

7   Mrs McArthy's urinalysis is **indicative** _____ a kidney infection.

8   The doctor was **concerned** _____ her liver function test results and referred her to a specialist.

9   People with low immunity are particularly **susceptible** _____ infection.

10 During a blood transfusion, you will receive a blood type which is **compatible** _____ your own blood type.

11 Are you **ready** _____ your shower?

12 I am recommending that you begin a diet which is **low** _____ sugar.

13 Mrs Murphy's son is **worried** _____ her memory. She has become very forgetful.

14 He was not **receptive** _____ the therapist's advice. Perhaps his wife can talk to him.

15 Mrs Quinn is very **upset** _____ her test results. Could you have the doctor call her?

16 The small intestine is **responsible** _____ absorbing nutrients.

GRAMMAR BOOST 3: VERBS + PREPOSITIONS

Examples of verb + preposition combinations

verb + on advise, base, concentrate, congratulate, decide, depend, focus, insist, operate, rely	• *An expert will **advise on** infection control at the seminar next week.* • *The gastroenterologist has recommended a colonoscopy **based on** your recent history of bowel problems.* • *We will need to **decide on** a date for the surgery.*
verb + for apply, arrange, ask, care, look, pay, prescribe, recommend, refer, wait	• *I will **arrange for** an ambulance to take you to hospital.* • *You will need to **pay for** the procedure on the day.* • *What treatment do you **recommend for** urticaria?* • *Your general practitioner may **refer** you **to** a specialist for additional tests.* • *Please **wait** here **for** the triage nurse.*
verb + of advise, consist, inform	• *The doctor will **advise** you **of** any changes to your medication.* • *The complimentary baby pack **consists of** baby care products and information for new parents.* • *Her family must be kept **informed of** her condition.*

verb + with agree, argue, assist, associate, collaborate, communicate, comply, confuse, consult, continue, cope, deal, diagnose, discuss, infect, interact, interfere, persist, present, proceed, provide	• Can you **assist with** this procedure? • Please **assist** Mrs Seymour **with** her exercises. • We suggest that you **discuss** new treatment options **with** the specialist. • Mrs Weng **presented with** acute back pain. • The pharmacy will **provide** you **with** medication for a month.
verb + in immerse, involve, participate, specialise	• **Immerse** your foot **in** cool water. • Ensure the patient is **involved in** the treatment plan.
verb + to adapt, adhere, belong, confess, entitle, expose, lead, link, listen, object, react, refer, relate, reply, talk	• It may take a few days for him to **adapt to** his new environment. • This drug **belongs to** the sulphonamides family. • Why is Mr Lee **objecting to** seeing a doctor? • I think my daughter may have **reacted to** the antibiotic. • The skin tear on his arm is **related to** the fall he had yesterday. • Are you **related to** the patient? • I have not **talked to** the doctor about her hearing loss yet.
verb + from abstain, benefit, differ, isolate, prevent, prohibit, protect, recover, recuperate, refrain, resign, suffer, withdraw	• The law **prohibits** people **from** smoking in hospitals. • How long does it take to fully **recover from** measles? • How long will it take to **recuperate from** these injuries? • You must **refrain from** drinking alcohol while taking this medication. • I do not **suffer from** migraine headaches.

verb + about	
complain, enquire, inform, inquire, know, learn, talk, worry	• I would like to **enquire about** travel vaccinations. • Have you been **informed about** the risks of this type of surgery?
verb + at	
look	• Could you please **look at** this wound? It is not healing.
verb + against	
advise, decide, immunise, protect, vaccinate	• You are **advised against** leaving the hospital before you are discharged by your doctor. • Why has Mr Hobbs **decided against** further treatment? • I am travelling overseas soon. Should I be **immunised against** Hepatitis A? • Covering the wound will help to **protect** it **against** infection.

PRACTICE 3: MATCHING SENTENCE BEGINNINGS AND ENDINGS

Match the beginning of sentences in Column A with the most suitable ending in Column B. Write your answers in the space provided. An example (0) has been done for you.

COLUMN A	COLUMN B
0 <u>Has Mr Burke decided</u>	A to a specialist?
1 Mrs Dawson is insisting	B about hiring a nebuliser from the chemist.
2 Does he need to be referred	C on more pain relief.
3 You need to enquire	D for a doctor to become available.
4 Mr Crane was diagnosed	E the most suitable dentures for you.
5 We need to wait	F from the surgery.
6 A dentist will be able to recommend	G with prostate cancer three months ago.
7 She recovered quickly	H for the medication I received in hospital?
8 Ouch! Could you look	I <u>**against having radiation therapy?**</u>
9 How do I pay	J at my finger? I think I have a splinter.

Write your answers here.

0	1	2	3	4	5	6	7	8	9
I									

PRACTICE 4: COMPLETE THE SENTENCE - VERB + PREPOSITION

Complete each sentence with the most suitable preposition. An example (0) has been done for you.

0   The doctor **prescribed** this inhaler <u>**for**</u> your asthma.

1   Several children at the childcare centre have been **infected** _____ norovirus.

2   Do you **react** _____ high-histamine foods?

3   Mrs Da Souza has been **suffering** _____ headaches for several days.

4   Does this shower chair **belong** _____ Mr Dutton?

5   The treatment will **depend** _____ the test results.

6   **Based** _____ your blood test results and scan, the obstetrician has recommended further testing.

7   Complications from pneumonia can **lead** _____ hospitalisation.

8   Have you **discussed** your treatment options _____ your family?

9   Nicholas Lawson was **diagnosed** _____ nephritis at the age of 3.

10 You may **benefit** _____ some physiotherapy.

11 How does sinusitis **differ** _____ a cold?

12 Is your child regularly **exposed** _____ second-hand cigarette smoke?

13 There are many negative health effects **associated** _____ taking illicit drugs.

14 Isolation is a method of infection control which aims to **prevent** infected patients _____ infecting others.

15 How is Mr Fulton **coping** _____ his soft diet?

16 It is recommended that all children are **immunised** _____ pneumococcal disease.

PRACTICE 5: CLOZE

Complete each sentence in the following text with the most suitable preposition. An example (0) has been done for you.

Many people are aware **(0)** <u>__of__</u> what they should be eating for good health, while others are not at all familiar (1) _____ recommended dietary guidelines.

Making the right food choices helps you to maintain a healthy weight. Experts say obesity is linked (2)_____ an increased risk of coronary heart disease and stroke, Type 2 diabetes and certain types of cancer. Eating a wide variety of foods provides your body (3)_____ the vitamins and minerals it needs and may also help protect against disease.

Experts recommend eating mostly plant-based foods. This means the majority of your diet should consist (4) _____ vegetables, fruit, wholegrain breads and cereals, legumes and pulses. These foods are rich

(5)_____ vitamins, minerals and fibre, which are all beneficial (6) _____ your health. They are also low (7) _____ sugar and fat. Lean beef, pork, poultry and fish should be consumed regularly. In fact, new research shows higher fish intake is consistently associated (8) _____ lower rates of heart disease. The amount of food you should eat depends (9) _____ your age, gender and activity levels.

If you are interested (10) _____ learning more, speak to a health professional.

PRACTICE 6: MULTIPLE CHOICE CLOZE

Read the following excerpt from a Patient Information Sheet about Magnetic Resonance Imaging (MRI). Choose the most suitable answer A, B or C to complete each sentence. An example (0) has been done for you.

Magnetic Resonance Imaging (MRI) Patient Information Sheet
Frequently Asked Questions (FAQs)

FAQ 1   What is magnetic resonance imaging?

Magnetic resonance imaging (MRI) is a diagnostic test that uses a magnetic field and radio waves to create images of organs and structures inside the body. MRI provides your doctor with valuable information to **(0) assist** with the diagnosis (or exclusion) of disease. MRI is (1) _____ from x-ray and certain conditions may (2) _____ you from having an MRI scan. Your doctor will advise you whether you are a (3) _____ candidate for MRI.

FAQ 2   Will I need to do any special preparation?

Usually, no preparation is required. If you are required to fast prior to your scan, you will be informed of this in advance.

FAQ 3   How long will the scan take?

This (4) _____ on the nature of the investigation and the part of the body being studied. Typically, an MRI scan takes approximately 30 minutes, but in some cases it may take up to an hour.

FAQ 4   When should I arrive for the procedure?

Please arrive 30 minutes before the scheduled time for your scan.

FAQ 5   What happens before the scan?

A technician will (5) _____ with you prior to the scan to check your details and answer any questions you have. Most patients will be asked to remove jewellery and change into a cotton gown before going into the scan room. You will be given a few moments to (6) _____ to your surroundings before the scanning commences. If you are claustrophobic

---

or feeling (7) _____ about the procedure, you may be prescribed a mild sedative. You may be able to (8) _____ to music through headphones during the scan. Ask the technician if this possible.

FAQ 6 Do I need to stay completely still during the scan?

You will need to (9) _____ from moving in order for the technician to obtain the clearest images. Images that are blurred may need to be retaken. In addition, if you move during the scan the part of your body we need to (10) _____ on may no longer be in the correct position.

FAQ 7 When will I get the results?

Your results will be available within 48 hours of the scan. A radiologist (a doctor who (11) _____ in evaluating medical images) will write a report and send it to the doctor who (12) _____ you for the scan. Please contact the referring doctor for your results.

0	**A** relate	**B** **assist**	**C** inform
1	**A** similar	**B** opposed	**C** different
2	**A** prevent	**B** refrain	**C** discontinue
3	**A** relevant	**B** capable	**C** suitable
4	**A** focuses	**B** consists	**C** depends
5	**A** consult	**B** inquire	**C** ask
6	**A** belong	**B** adjust	**C** recover
7	**A** anxious	**B** afraid	**C** unsuitable
8	**A** focus	**B** hear	**C** listen
9	**A** refrain	**B** prevent	**C** proceed
10	**A** base	**B** focus	**C** depend
11	**A** specialises	**B** interested	**C** concentrates
12	**A** prescribed	**B** responsible	**C** referred

SETTING: BAYSIDE ASTHMA ASSOCIATION

Read the advertisement about a seminar on asthma to be presented by the Bayside Asthma Association. Notice the *word forms* in bold below.

The Bayside Asthma Association provides the community with up-to-date **information** about asthma through its website, printed leaflets and **monthly** educational seminars.

The next seminar will be held at the Bayside Asthma Association's office on Tuesday.

Topics to be addressed include:

- common causes of asthma
- risks of living with **undiagnosed** asthma
- **recurrent** symptoms associated with asthma e.g. **breathlessness** and wheezing
- long-term preventative **treatment**
- findings of **recently** published research

Register today for this free **informative** seminar.

If you would like to **donate** to the Bayside Asthma Association, you can do this online or in person. All **donations** are used to fund further asthma research.

Look at the highlighted words (in bold) in the Bayside Asthma Association advertisement. Look at the table below to see which form of the words is used.

VERB	NOUN	ADJECTIVE	ADVERB
	information	informative	
			monthly
		undiagnosed	
		recurrent	
	breathlessness		
donate	donations		
	treatment		
			recently

GRAMMAR BOOST 1: WORD FORM RECOGNITION

Word formation and word recognition skills will help you to make appropriate choices of language in your spoken and written communication.

When learning new vocabulary, you are recommended to use a dictionary:

- to explore the meaning of the root word.
- to note other commonly used forms of the word - verb, noun, adjective and adverb.
- to become familiar with prefixes which can be used to change the meaning of the root word.

Look at how different forms of the words are used in the example sentences below.

1 Verb	You are expected **to recover** from the surgery in about 5 days.
2 Noun	Your **recovery** from the surgery is expected to take about five days.

1 Verb	Remove the dressing carefully so that you do not **traumatise** the new tissue.
2 Noun	He was taken to hospital with chest and abdominal **trauma** following the car accident.
3 Adjective	The death of her mother was a very **traumatic** event in her life.
4 Prefix with adjective	The paramedic was diagnosed with **post-traumatic** stress disorder. (post-traumatic = suffering trauma **after** an event or a series of events)

1 Adjective	The patient was **conscious** during the dental implant procedure.
2 Prefix with adjective	Harriet was **unconscious** for a few minutes after hitting her head when she fell off the ladder. (unconscious = **not** conscious)

1 Adjective	Side effects of this medication are **reversible** and will disappear after the treatment is complete. (reversible = will improve)
2 Prefix with adjective	The stroke caused **irreversible** brain damage. (irreversible = describes the brain damage which can**not** be reversed or improved)
3 Prefix with adverb	The brain was **irreversibly** damaged by the stroke. (irreversibly damaged = describes the brain which was **permanently damaged** and can**not** recover)

1 Verb	*People with a family history of cancer were asked **to volunteer** in a survey.*
2 Noun	*Training to become a **volunteer** at the hospital takes place every month.*
3 Adjective	*Participation in the medical trials is on a **voluntary** basis.*
4 Prefix with adjective	*Neurological disorders may cause **involuntary** muscle spasms.* (**involuntary** = unable to be controlled)
5 Adverb	*The patient **voluntarily** joined the exercise program to increase his fitness level.*
6 Prefix with adverb	*He was **involuntarily** committed to a mental health unit following assessment of his mental condition by the medical team.*

BOOSTER TIP - RECOGNISING WORD FORMS

There are no simple rules to guide you in word formation. However, there are some common *endings* that will help you recognise **verb**, **noun**, or **adjective** forms. Look at the examples in the tables.

COMMON VERB ENDINGS	
ENDINGS	**EXAMPLES**
-ain	sust**ain**, abst**ain**, maint**ain**, constr**ain**, dr**ain**, ret**ain**
-ate	deterior**ate**, medic**ate**, urin**ate**, vaccin**ate**, regul**ate**, resuscit**ate**, hydr**ate**, dil**ate**, coagul**ate**, disloc**ate**, gest**ate**, termin**ate**
-en	strength**en**, sharp**en**, wors**en**, weak**en**, straight**en**, deep**en**
-er	administ**er**, ref**er**, transf**er**, consid**er**, def**er**, deliv**er**, alt**er**
-ict	constr**ict**, restr**ict**, pred**ict**
-ify	calc**ify**, pac**ify**, simpl**ify**, ident**ify**
-ine	determ**ine**, exam**ine**
-ise (usually British English)	apolog**ise**, orga**nise**, hospital**ise**, cauter**ise**, nebul**ise**, steril**ise**
-ize (usually American English)	apolog**ize**, orga**nize**, hospital**ize**, cauter**ize**, nebul**ize**, steril**ize**
-ise (British/American English)	circum**cise**, in**cise**, pract**ise**
-ish	nour**ish**, establ**ish**, fin**ish**, extingu**ish**
-ure	reass**ure**, end**ure**
-y	appl**y**, reappl**y**

COMMON NOUN ENDINGS	
ENDINGS	**EXAMPLES**
-age	blockage, drainage, haemorrhage
-ance	assistance, maintenance, ambulance, appearance, avoidance
-dom	wisdom, boredom, freedom, condom
-edge	knowledge
-ema	emphysema, enema, oedema, eczema
-ence	dependence, patience, incontinence, recurrence, pre-existence, flatulence, abstinence
-er	inhaler, spacer, nebuliser, audiometer, caliper
-hood	childhood, adulthood, likelihood, livelihood
-ia	dementia, analgesia, anaesthesia, bacteria, paranoia, anaemia, dyslexia, leukaemia
-iac	coeliac, haemophiliac
-ice	practice, advice, hospice, malpractice, jaundice
-ief	relief, grief, belief
-ing	nursing, misunderstanding
-ion	inflammation, medication, reaction, constipation, sensation, distension, complication
-ism	autism, alcoholism, embolism, rheumatism, metabolism, hyperthyroidism
-ist	psychiatrist, optometrist, dentist, oncologist, physiotherapist, gastroenterologist
-itis	hepatitis, bronchiolitis, bursitis, appendicitis, conjunctivitis, sinusitis
-ity	fertility, quality, obesity, mobility, agility, activity, irritability, priority, sensitivity
-ment	improvement, management, supplement, treatment, nourishment, ligament
-ness	cleanliness, illness, drowsiness, tightness, weakness, faintness, consciousness
-oma	glaucoma, stoma, fibroma, carcinoma, coma
-or	ventilator, indicator, bronchodilator, vasodilator, chiropractor, operator
-sis	diagnosis, analysis, dialysis, fibrosis, scoliosis, sepsis, amniocentesis, thrombosis
-ure	exposure, acupuncture, denture, seizure, venipuncture, suture, pressure, signature
-y	psychiatry, allergy, microbiology, recovery, pregnancy, malignancy, endoscopy, dentistry, gastroenterology, surgery, privacy

COMMON ADJECTIVE ENDINGS

ENDINGS	EXAMPLES
-able	treat**able**, prevent**able**, adjust**able**, notice**able**, uncomfort**able**, sustain**able**, advis**able**
-al	bacteri**al**, clinic**al**, typic**al**, umbilic**al**, vir**al**, fung**al**, psychologic**al**, visu**al**, gastrointestin**al**
-ar	mol**ar**, vascul**ar**, bipol**ar**, molecul**ar**, ocul**ar**, nucle**ar**, granul**ar**, cellul**ar**
-ful	pain**ful**, harm**ful**, stress**ful**, plenti**ful**, success**ful**, use**ful**
-iac	card**iac**, sacroil**iac**
-ic	letharg**ic**, allerg**ic**, chron**ic**, epilept**ic**, metastat**ic**, microscop**ic**, dyslex**ic**, opt**ic**
-ient	impat**ient**, conven**ient**, inconven**ient**, trans**ient**
-ile	ster**ile**, mob**ile**, febr**ile**, juven**ile**, tact**ile**, ag**ile**, infert**ile**
-ive	preventat**ive**, addict**ive**, extens**ive**, digest**ive**, accumulat**ive**, addict**ive**, inclus**ive**, invas**ive**, laxat**ive**, prescript**ive**, derivat**ive**
-less	pain**less**, harm**less**, life**less**, weight**less**, taste**less**, colour**less**, odour**less**
-oid	paran**oid**, subarachn**oid**, rheumat**oid**
-ory	sens**ory**, respirat**ory**, compuls**ory**, inflammat**ory**, satisfact**ory**
-ous	cancer**ous**, danger**ous**, nause**ous**, cutane**ous**, semiconsci**ous**, contagi**ous**
-y	drows**y**, hungr**y**, thirst**y**, dizz**y**, melanchol**y**

PRACTICE 1: IDENTIFYING VERBS, NOUNS AND ADJECTIVES

Decide whether the underlined words in bold in the following sentences are used as verbs, nouns or adjectives. Write verb, noun or adjective in the space provided at the end of each sentence. An example (0) has been done for you.

0   The patient was admitted to hospital with **appendicitis.**   __NOUN__

1   The ophthalmologist will use drops to **dilate** your pupils before examining your eyes.   _____

2   High grade tumours are often fast-growing and may require **aggressive** treatment.   _____

3   The local hospice provides **palliative** care for terminally ill patients.   _____

4   You should avoid **strenuous** exercise for six weeks after major abdominal surgery.   _____

5   The **orthodontist** fitted the teenager with braces for her teeth.   _____

6   Anti-inflammatory medication may temporarily **alleviate** arthritic pain in knee joints.   _____

7   **Astigmatism** can usually be corrected through the use of glasses or contact lenses.   _____

8   Hospital staff will **notify** next-of-kin if the patient's condition deteriorates.   _____

9   If you are diagnosed with **hypertension**, you may be advised to change your lifestyle.   _____

10 The patient discussed his **prognosis** with the specialist.   _____

11 A diet rich in anti-oxidants may help to slow the progress of **macular** degeneration.   _____

12 There was an outbreak of a highly **infectious** form of gastroenteritis at the local school. _____

GRAMMAR BOOST 2: TRANSFORMING WORD FORMS – ADJECTIVE TO NOUN

EXAMPLES OF *ADJECTIVE* AND *NOUN* FORMS	
ADJECTIVE	**NOUN**
addicted (to), addictive	addict/addiction
allergic	allergy
angry	anger
anxious	anxiety
bacterial	bacteria
dental	dentist/dentistry
disabled	disability
harmful/harmless	harm
hungry	hunger
infectious	infection
lethargic	lethargy
mobile	mobility
painful/painless	pain
pharmaceutical	pharmacy/pharmacist
professional	profession/professional
psychological	psychology/psychologist
red	redness
safe/unsafe	safety
surgical	surgery/surgeon
tender	tenderness
viral	virus

PRACTICE 2: ADJECTIVE OR NOUN?

Look carefully at each of the following sentences. Choose and <u>underline</u> the most suitable noun or adjective form in brackets to complete each sentence. An example (0) has been done for you.

0   Health and (safe / **safety**) regulations must be followed in the workplace.

1   Look out for signs of (infectious / infection) at the wound site. If there is any (red / redness) or (tender / tenderness), contact your doctor.

2   People who are (allergic / allergy) to peanuts are advised to keep an epinephrine autoinjector with them at all times.

3   You are scheduled for your (dental / dentist) procedure in the (surgical / surgery / surgeon) on Tuesday.

4   The senior (pharmaceutical / pharmacy / pharmacist) in the local (pharmaceutical / pharmacy / pharmacist) places weekly orders for new (pharmaceutical / pharmacy / pharmacist) supplies.

5   (Bacterial / Bacteria) conjunctivitis can be treated with antibiotic eye drops.

GRAMMAR BOOST 3: TRANSFORMING WORD FORMS – VERB TO NOUN

EXAMPLES OF *VERB* AND *NOUN* FORMS	
VERB	**NOUN**
admit	admission
advise	advice
arrive	arrival
complain	complaint
consult	consultation/consultant
deteriorate	deterioration
dress	dressing
enter	entrance
expect	expectation
feel	feeling
improve	improvement
infect	infection
inflame	inflammation
manage	management/manager
medicate	medication
obstruct	obstruction

prescribe	prescription
recover	recovery
rehabilitate	rehabilitation
refer	referral
sedate	sedation
treat	treatment
urinate	urination
vaccinate	vaccination

PRACTICE 3: VERB OR NOUN?

Look carefully at each of the following sentences. Choose and <u>underline</u> the most suitable verb or noun form (Option A or Option B) to complete each sentence. An example (0) has been done for you.

0   The nurse was directed to _____ the wound every day.

   A   **<u>dress</u>**   B   dressing

1   An _____ in the lower bowel was detected during the colonoscopy.

   A   obstruct   B   obstruction

2   The patient had a fever and was suffering from excessive _____.

   A   urinate   B   urination

3   If your condition does not _____ , you will be admitted to hospital.

   A   improve   B   improvement

4   Bring the _____ from your doctor with you to the appointment with the cardiologist.

   A   refer   B   referral

5   Specialised tests are available which can help your doctor _____ the cause of your allergy.

   A   diagnose   B   diagnosis

6   We would like to _____ your father in the clinic overnight for signs of sleep apnoea.

   A   observe   B   observation

7   This medication is available by _____ only.

   A   prescribe   B   prescription

8   You are required to complete this form before your _____ to the hospital.

   A   admit   B   admission

GRAMMAR BOOST 4: TRANSFORMING WORD FORMS - VERB TO NOUN TO ADJECTIVE

EXAMPLES OF *VERB, NOUN* AND *ADJECTIVE* FORMS		
VERB	**NOUN**	**ADJECTIVE**
adhere	adhesion	adhesive (tape)
assist	assistance	assisted/unassisted
customise	customisation	customised
depend	dependence/independence	dependent/independent
depress	depression	depressed
diagnose	diagnosis	diagnostic
disappoint	disappointment	disappointed
help	help	helpful/unhelpful
infect	infection	infectious
inform	information	informative
medicate	medication	medicated
motivate	motivation	motivational/unmotivated/ motivated/motivating
observe	observation	observable/observant/ unobserved
progress	progress, progression	progressive
specialise	specialist, specialisation	specialist
use	use	useful/useless

PRACTICE 4: VERB, NOUN OR ADJECTIVE?

Read the following leaflet about the Pines Centre Rehabilitation Facility. Choose the most suitable verb, noun or adjective form of the word given in brackets to complete each sentence in the following text. An example (0) has been done for you.

WELCOME TO THE PINES CENTRE

We hope that you will find this leaflet **(0) useful (use)** and (1)_____ (**inform**).

Following your discharge from hospital, you will be transferred to the Pines Centre for intensive post-operative (2)_____ (**rehabilitate**).

The Pines Centre offers a (3) _____ (**custom**) program designed to support the most effective (4) _____ (**recover**) for each individual patient.

On (5)_____ (**arrive**) at the Centre, you will be introduced to the team of (6)_____ (**profession**) case managers who will be responsible for managing your program and monitoring your progress.

It is important for patients to understand the key milestones of their program as they regain their (7)_____ (**depend**). Patients who have unrealistic (8)_____ (**expect**) of the time required for their recuperation may become (9)_____ (**anxiety**) and (10)_____ (**depress**) if they feel their progress is too slow. Case managers encourage patients to remain (11) _____ (**motivate**) in order to recover as quickly as possible.

Some (12)_____(**help**) hints for you to maintain a positive outlook are:

- follow the (13) _____ (**advise**) of your case managers.

- eat a (14) _____ (**health**) diet.

- commit to your daily exercise program.

- stay (15) _____ (**connect**) to your family and friends by phone or via social media.

For further (16) _____ (**inform**) or (17) _____ (**assist**), please ask our staff.

GRAMMAR BOOST 5: TRANSFORMING WORD FORMS – ADJECTIVE TO ADVERB

An adverb can be used to give more information about a verb and/or an adjective. An adverb is often formed by adding –ly to the end of an adjective. Note important changes in spelling in the examples given, for example, *irresponsible becomes irresponsibly*, *angry becomes angrily*.

PRACTICE 5: TRANSFORMING WORD FORMS - ADJECTIVES AND ADVERBS

Complete the table with the correct form of the missing adjectives or adverbs. Two examples, (0) and (00), have been done for you.

	EXAMPLES OF *ADJECTIVE* AND *ADVERB* FORMS	
	ADJECTIVE	**ADVERB**
0	**angry**	angrily
00	irresponsible	**irresponsibly**

1	accidental	
2	anxious	
3	final	
4		independently
5	unexpected	
6		usually
7		comfortably
8	hungry	
9		tenderly
10	psychological	
11		surgically
12	painful	

BOOSTER TIP - ADJECTIVE OR ADVERB?

The frequency words below use the same form when the word functions as an adjective or as an adverb. Look at the examples.

daily	daily
• *You need to take a **daily** dose of this medication.* (adjective)	• *You need to take this medicine three times **daily**.* (adverb)
hourly	hourly
• *A nurse conducts **hourly** checks on the patients in this hospital.* (adjective)	• *Observations are recorded **hourly** after surgery.* (adverb)
weekly	weekly
• *The midwife holds **weekly** antenatal classes.* (adjective)	• *Do you see the speech pathologist **weekly**?* (adverb)

PRACTICE 6: ADJECTIVE OR ADVERB?

Look carefully at each of the following sentences. Choose and <u>underline</u> the most suitable adjective or adverb form (Option A or Option B) to complete each sentence. An example (0) has been done for you.

0   You should eat fresh fruit and vegetables _____.

    A   regular   **B   <u>regularly</u>**

1   This medication is to be taken _____ before meals.

    A   oral   B   orally

2   The nurse recorded a _____ increase in the patient's temperature.

    A   significant   B   significantly

3   I have trouble remembering events that have happened _____.

    A   recent   B   recently

4   _____ influenza vaccinations are given free-of-charge to people who are at serious risk of contracting the illness.

    A   Annual   B   Annually

5   The driver sustained _____ injuries when the bus overturned.

    A   serious   B   seriously

6   This topical steroid cream is very strong. Use it _____.

    A   sparing   B   sparingly

GRAMMAR BOOST 6: USING PREFIXES TO CHANGE MEANING

Prefixes can be used to change the meaning of verbs, nouns, adjectives and adverbs. The most common prefix is *un*, which means 'not'. Other common prefixes include: *in, il, im, in, ir, pre, post, ante, anti, ab, mal, de, mis, trans, sub, hyper, hypo, intra.*

Look at the examples below to see how prefixes can change the meaning of these words.

PREFIX	EXAMPLE WORD	NEW WORD	MEANING
in	dependent (adjective)	independent	**not** dependent
il	literate (adjective)	illiterate	**cannot** read or write
ir	regular (adjective)	irregular	**not** regular
im	possibility (noun)	impossibility	**not** a possibility
un	responsive (adjective)	unresponsive	**not** responsive
mis	understand (verb)	misunderstand	**cannot** understand accurately
de	regulate (verb)	deregulate	**remove** (the regulation)
anti	histamine (noun)	antihistamine	**reduces the effect of** (histamine) against/opposite
mal	practice (noun)	malpractice	**bad, poor, wrong** (practice)
trans	plant (verb or noun)	transplant	**move** something across to another place/person
pre, ante	natal (adjective)	prenatal antenatal	**before** (birth)
post	natal (adjective)	postnatal	**after** (birth)
ab	normality (noun)	abnormality	something **not** expected, **un**usual, **not** normal
sub	cutaneous (adjective)	subcutaneous	**below, under** (the skin)
hyper	ventilate (verb)	hyperventilate	**over, above, more than normal** (breathing rate)
hypo	glycaemia (noun)	hypoglycaemia	**below, less than normal** (blood sugar level)
intra	cranial (adjective)	intracranial	**within, inside** (the brain)
inter	cellular (adjective)	intercellular	**between** (cells)
a	typical (adjective)	atypical	**not** typical

PRACTICE 7: USING PREFIXES

Choose a prefix from Box A and add the prefix to a base word from Box B. Write the new word (prefix + base word) in Box C. You will use each prefix and each base word only once.
Two examples, (00) and (0), have been done for you.

A	intra	post	im	mal	de	mis
	in	pre	un	trans	anti	hyper

B					
	venous	fibrillator	coagulant	maturity	mission
	eclampsia	conscious	**operative**	allergenic	carriage
		fertile		nutrition	

C	0	intravenous		
	00	postoperative		
	1		6	
	2		7	
	3		8	
	4		9	
	5		10	

PRACTICE 8: COMPLETE THE SENTENCE

Choose the most suitable word from the box to complete each sentence. An example (0) has been done for you.

transplant	**antibiotics**	atypical	hypotension
antenatal	vaccinations	incontinence	unassisted
irregularly	dehydrated	transfusion	

0   The doctor prescribed a course of **antibiotics** to treat the infection.

1   After experiencing significant blood loss in the accident, the patient required a blood
_____.

2   _____ classes for pregnant women are conducted at the local health clinic
on Tuesdays.

3   Specialist products, such as disposable pants, pads and liners, can be purchased for people
suffering from urinary _____ to help them stay dry and lead a normal life.

4   If you have heart palpitations or you feel like your heart is beating _____,
you should visit your doctor for a check-up.

5   You can be discharged when you are able to walk up and down the stairs _____.

6   _____ cells should be investigated further for signs of
malignancy.

7   The surgeon was notified when a donor organ became available for _____.

8   Maintain your fluid intake during the physiotherapy sessions so that you do not become
_____.

9 Have you asked your doctor about the recommended_____
for the countries you intend to visit?

10 Suffering from shock following the surgical procedure, the patient displayed symptoms of
_____ including dizziness, nausea and blurred vision.

PRACTICE 9: WORD FORMATION

Read the following leaflet about skin cancer. Choose the most suitable form of the word given in bold at the end of the line to complete each sentence. You may choose the verb, noun, adjective or adverb form of the word. You may also need to add a prefix. An example (0) has been done for you.

SKIN CANCER AWARENESS	
Early **(0)** <u>detection</u> of skin cancer (1) _____ leads to increased (2)_____ rates.	**(0) detect** **(1) general** **(2) survive**
Following (3) _____ to the sun over long periods of time, normal cells in the skin can change into (4) _____ cells which multiply (5)_____ throughout the body.	**(3) expose** **(4) normal** **(5) control**

Protecting your skin against sun damage

- Always wear (6) _____clothing when outside in the sun.

(6) protect

- Apply sunscreen to all areas exposed to the sun before exercising or (7)_____ outdoor sport.

(7) play

- Have your skin checked (8)_____.

(8) regular

Detecting skin cancer

- Become familiar with your skin.

- Look for any changes in spots on the skin – changes in colour, size or (9)_____.

(9) appear

- If you notice anything (10) _____, see your doctor immediately.

(10) usual

- The doctor will take a biopsy of the spot to send to an experienced (11)_____ for (12)_____.

(11) pathology
(12) analyse

Treating skin cancer

- The most common treatment is surgical (13) _____ with a wide excision of (14) _____ tissue.

(13) remove
(14) surround

- Other available (15) _____ include:

(15) treat

  *chemotherapy ointments for non-melanoma cancers

  *radiotherapy for skin cancers near the eyes or on the nose or forehead

If left (16) _____, skin cancer can be life-threatening.

(16) treat

PRACTICE 1: MATCHING QUESTIONS AND ANSWERS

SETTING: HOSPITAL OBSTETRICS UNIT

A patient is having a procedure following a missed miscarriage. Match each question in Column A with the most suitable response in Column B. Write your answers in the space provided. An example (0) has been done for you.

COLUMN A	COLUMN B
0 <u>**What is your name?**</u>	A No, I stopped 3 days ago.
1 What is your date of birth?	B A dilation and curettage.
2 Who is your general practitioner?	C My partner is coming for me.
3 How are you feeling?	D <u>**Antonella Fiori.**</u>
4 What procedure are you having today?	E Just folic acid and a probiotic.
5 Have you had this procedure before?	F Not too bad, thanks.
6 When did you last have something to eat or drink?	G October 16, 1985.
7 Do you take any regular medication or supplements?	H At dinner last night. I have not had anything to eat or drink since 8 o'clock last night.
8 Did you take any this morning?	I No, this is my first.
9 Have you ever had a reaction to an anaesthetic?	J My blood pressure was a little low after an anaesthetic once.
10 How will you be getting home after the procedure today?	K Dr Veronica Sim.

Write your answers here.

0	1	2	3	4	5	6	7	8	9	10
D										

PRACTICE 2: COMPLETE THE SENTENCE

Read the following correspondence from Dr Davidson regarding Mrs Yamada. Choose and <u>underline</u> the most suitable word to complete each sentence. An example (0) has been done for you.

Mrs Yoshiko Yamada is the patient. Dr Davidson is the gastroenterologist. Dr Perez is the referring general practitioner.

Letter 1

Dear Mrs Yamada

You **(0) had** / *had had* a colonoscopy and polypectomy performed today.

Please see (1) *the / an* attached report for information regarding your procedure.

Please make (2) *an / the* appointment to see Dr Davidson for follow up. Recommendations based (3) *of / on* today's investigations will be discussed at this appointment.

As you may suffer (4) *some / any* drowsiness or dizziness after the sedation, it (5) *is / was* advisable to have a responsible adult remain with you overnight. You may now cease your low residue diet and resume your (6) *regularly / regular* eating habits.

As you have (7) *had / been* intravenous sedation you must not drive a vehicle, make important decisions or sign any legal documents for twenty-four (8) *hour / hours*.

If you experience pain, bleeding or have any (9) *concern / concerns* following this procedure, please attend the Cityside Private Hospital Emergency Centre where there is a gastroenterologist on call.

(10) *In case / Provided* you have no post procedural complications, we will see you at your follow-up appointment.

Yours sincerely
Dr William Davidson

Letter 2

Dear Dr Perez

Re: Yoshiko Yamada

Indication: Pain over left inguinal crease

Colonoscopy findings: The instrument (11) *was / were* inserted through the colon to the terminal ileum. The bowel preparation (12) *was / has* good and the patient tolerated the procedure well. A careful inspection was made on insertion and slow removal of the instrument. No (13) *complications / complication* occurred during or immediately post procedure.

Three polyps measuring 5-6 millimetres were removed from the sigmoid colon by snare without diathermy. No (14) *other / another* abnormalities were detected. Multiple biopsies were taken for pathology. I (15) *am / will* awaiting the results.

Thank you for referring this patient (16) *to / for* Cityside Private Gastroenterology.

Yours sincerely
Dr William Davidson

PRACTICE 3: MULTIPLE CHOICE CLOZE

Text 1: Blood specimen collection

Read the following text about blood specimen collection. Choose the most suitable answer A, B or C to complete each sentence. An example (0) has been done for you.

First, positively identify **(0) <u>the</u>** patient and ensure they have the correct requisition form for the procedure. Ensure all patient preparation, for example, fasting, (1) _____ been done correctly. (2) _____ the required preparation has not been (3) _____ according to the instructions, the procedure will need to be postponed. Many patients experience some anxiety when having blood taken. (4) _____ the patient about the procedure and reassure them as necessary.

Next, gather the tubes or containers and other supplies needed for the draw and ensure the patient (5) _____ positioned appropriately. Sitting upright is most common but lying down should be (6) _____ for patients at risk of fainting. Apply a tourniquet or cuff and ensure it is not too tight. Put on non-latex gloves, palpate for a vein and identify a suitable site (7) _____ puncture. After the puncture site has been selected, cleanse the area and allow it to dry. Ask the patient to make a fist. Insert the needle swiftly through the skin and into the vein. Release the tourniquet or cuff as the last tube or container (8) _____ being filled. Withdraw the needle (9) _____ the patient's arm, immediately place gauze on the puncture site and apply gentle pressure. Ensure (10) _____ tubes and containers have had the correct labels affixed. After approximately two minutes, check the puncture site and cover it with gauze. Observe the patient for (11)_____ after effects such as bleeding from the site or fainting. Discard all (12) _____ materials used in the procedure in the designated containers.

0	**A** some	**B** <u>the</u>	**C** a
1	**A** have	**B** has	**C** was
2	**A** Provided	**B** Unless	**C** If
3	**A** complete	**B** completed	**C** completion
4	**A** Explain	**B** Discuss	**C** Inform
5	**A** is	**B** are	**C** were
6	**A** considered	**B** consideration	**C** consider
7	**A** in	**B** with	**C** for
8	**A** is	**B** are	**C** be
9	**A** for	**B** from	**C** about
10	**A** any	**B** each	**C** all
11	**A** all	**B** any	**C** some
12	**A** contaminated	**B** contamination	**C** contaminate

Text 2: Letter of Discharge

Read the following Letter of Discharge. Choose the most suitable answer A, B, or C to complete each sentence. An example (0) has been done for you.

Mr Simon Wong
Respite Centre Manager
Westside Respite Centre
45 Long Street, Westside

6 May (year)

Dear Mr Wong

Re: Bianca Anderson, aged 80

Mrs Bianca Anderson is **(0) _being_** discharged from Fairhome Hospital into your care for a period of 3 weeks, from 6 May to 27 May.

Mrs Anderson was admitted (1) _____ the Emergency Department via ambulance on 2 May (year) following (2)_____ at her home. She was found by her son, Matthew Anderson, who came to her aid when her personal alarm system was activated.

Mrs Anderson lives (3)_____ in her own home. She wants to remain as (4)_____as possible. She (5)_____ 3 times a week. According to her son, she is becoming forgetful and is not eating regularly. She has been mobile with the use of a walking stick but is becoming more unstable. Her son (6)_____ her daily by telephone.

On examination, Mrs Anderson appeared thin and dehydrated. She was slightly confused and there was (7)_____ to the right hip area. Her temperature, pulse and respiration rates were normal. Her blood pressure was elevated. Her dentures were loose. She was experiencing pain in her right hip related (8)_____ her fall and has ongoing knee pain.

(9)_____ fracture was detected in an x-ray of the right hip. Blood tests (full blood count) and urine tests (microurine) were unremarkable. Paracetamol was administered as needed for pain relief. Normal saline was administered intravenously (1 litre over 12 (10)_____) to treat dehydration. The use of a denture fixative was recommended to assist (11)_____ chewing. An emollient cream was applied to her skin twice a day.

Following 4 days in hospital, Mrs Anderson has become more lucid and her blood pressure has returned to normal. She has gained weight with regular meals and the use of a denture fixative. She (12)_____ to her general practitioner for a medication review.

The physiotherapist (13)_____ a wheelie walker with good effect. Mrs Anderson requires supervision to transfer and mobilise safely. Her son will organise the hire of a wheelie walker prior to discharge.

Please continue with her usual medications (see medication chart). (14)_____ pain persists, please contact her general practitioner. Please monitor for signs of dehydration and malnutrition.

Following respite care, Mrs Anderson will be discharged into her son's care. The social worker recommends (15)_____ for assisted living leading to permanent care.

Please do not hesitate to contact me if you require any further (16)_____ .

Yours sincerely
Esmerelda Lopez
Nurse in Charge

0	**A** be	**B** been	**C** <u>**being**</u>
1	**A** to	**B** for	**C** with
2	**A** fall	**B** the fall	**C** a fall
3	**A** alone	**B** lonely	**C** loneliness
4	**A** independence	**B** independent	**C** independently
5	**A** has delivered meals	**B** has meals delivered	**C** been delivered meals
6	**A** contacts	**B** contact	**C** contacting
7	**A** bruising	**B** bruise	**C** bruises
8	**A** by	**B** to	**C** with
9	**A** None	**B** Any	**C** No
10	**A** hours	**B** hour	**C** hourly
11	**A** with	**B** for	**C** to
12	**A** has referred	**B** has had referred	**C** has been referred
13	**A** has been trialled	**B** was trialled	**C** has trialled
14	**A** Unless	**B** If	**C** Provided that
15	**A** assessed	**B** assessment	**C** be assessed
16	**A** informations	**B** pieces information	**C** information

PRACTICE 4: SENTENCE TRANSFORMATION

Complete the second sentence so that it has a similar meaning to the first sentence. Use the word in bold. Do not change the word in bold. Use between 2 and 5 words including the word in bold. An example (0) has been done for you.

0   **be**

Mrs Kendall needs to have a psychiatric evaluation.

Mrs Kendall _____ **needs to be evaluated by** _____ a psychiatrist.

1   **never**

This is the first time I have had problems with this medication.

I _____ with this medication before.

2   **not**

She will have to go to hospital unless she gains weight.

She will have to go to hospital _____ weight.

3   **will**

The surgical team will make the decision tomorrow.

The decision_____ the surgical team tomorrow.

4 **case**

The doctor may ask to see your scans, so take them with you to your appointment.

Take your scans to your appointment _____
to see them.

5 **since**

Mr Johnson last had a spasm in his lower back 5 weeks ago.

It_____ Mr Johnson last had a spasm in his lower back.

6 **scale**

How severe is your pain?

Can you rate your_____ 1 to 10?

7 **first**

How long ago did you first notice these symptoms?

When _____ notice these symptoms?

8 **does**

What is your baby's weight?

How _____ ?

9 **low**

Her potassium levels were low due to an episode of acute gastroenteritis.

She _____ potassium due to an episode of acute
gastroenteritis.

10 **have**

I had been vomiting all night so I did not go to work.

If I had not been vomiting all night, I _____ to work.

11 **have**

A urinary catheter will be inserted during surgery.

You will _____ during surgery.

12 **is**

They are closely monitoring his condition following the infection.

His condition _____ following the infection.

PRACTICE 5: ERROR CORRECTION

Look carefully at each line in the following texts. Some of the lines are correct and some contain one extra word which should not be there. If a line is correct, put a tick (✔) in the space provided at the end of the line. If a line has an extra word that should not be there, write the word in the space provided at the end of the line. One example (0) in each text has been done for you.

Text 1: Professional development seminar: Medication adherence - a case study

0	Mr Huang, a 45 year old accountant, suffers from a chronic health conditions	a
1	(hypertension and diabetes) and takes multiple medications. He has started	
2	a new medication last month. He ceased taking the new medication after two	
3	weeks as he thought it was either not been working or having no effect. He	
4	developed tachycardia, elevated blood pressure and light-headedness. He was	
5	being in moderate distress caused by the rapid onset of his symptoms.	
6	What the reasons for his non adherence to the medication were investigated.	
7	He was an educated on the importance of taking medications as directed. The	
8	potential health implications of suddenly stopping his medication were	
9	explained. If he was advised that it may take several weeks to adjust to the new	
10	medication. He was counselled not to stop taking any medications unless not	
11	directed to do so by a doctor. Interventions were recommended to improve	
12	with medication adherence, including dispensary packs, text message	
13	reminders, electronic applications and the regular nurse feedback. He was	
14	referred to his general practitioner for a medication review.	

Text 2: Patient summary

0	At 21.30, Mr Thomas Vo experienced sharp left sided chest pain while he was	✔
1	lying in bed. He rated the pain 6 out of 10. The pain was lasted for 7 minutes.	
2	He experienced a breathlessness and felt dizzy and weak. The pain was	
3	non radiating. There was no nausea or vomiting and no loss of consciousness.	
4	Mr Vo reported the pain was similar to on previous chest pain. Mr Vo	
5	is now pain free and has no difficulty breathing. No analgesia was	
6	administered. Mr Vo has travelled on a 10 hour flight yesterday. Clinically,	
7	provided there are no signs of pulmonary embolism. He looks well and there is	

8	no leg swelling. He is not an hypoxic. His heart rate is 65 beats per minute.	
9	Chest x-rays and another blood tests were unremarkable. Mr Vo is to follow up	
10	with his general practitioner this week. He requires a stress test and other	
11	appropriate investigations as an outpatient to exclude Acute Coronary Syndrome.	

PRACTICE 6: WORD FORMATION

Read the following Letter of Discharge. Choose the most suitable form of the word given in bold at the end of the line to complete each sentence. An example (0) has been done for you.

Dear Dr Miles

Chloe Amelia Fairchild **(0) <u>presented</u>** to the Emergency Department at City Children's Hospital on 28 July (year) at 0228.

(0) present

The (1) _____ was headache.

(1) diagnose

Recently she has been (2) _____ unwell, feeling lethargic with occasional (3) _____ pain over the last few days, associated with mild rhinorrhea and cough. She began experiencing headache earlier tonight and felt hot at the time.

(2) general

(3) abdomen

On (4) _____ , Chloe was comfortable, alert, playful and happy.

(4) examine

Her vital signs were stable and she was afebrile. Her ear, nose and throat examination showed a (5)_____erythematous pharynx. Chest and abdomen exams were unremarkable. There were no signs of meningism. Nursing (6)_____ consisted of administering a single dose of children's paracetamol.

(5) mild

(6) manage

I have (7)_____ the case with the Emergency Department registrar and our impression is that of a likely (8) _____ infection causing headaches. We have advised rest, paracetamol/ibuprofen and fluids with (9) _____ to re-present should her symptoms (10) _____.

(7) discuss

(8) virus

(9) instruct

(10) worse

Thanks for your ongoing care.

Kind regards
Ravi Patel
Senior House Doctor

ANSWER KEY

UNIT 1   QUESTIONS

Practice 1: Matching questions and answers

ACCIDENT and EMERGENCY- Patient 1

0   B   How did you sustain your injuries?
1   C   Were you feeling dizzy before you fell?
2   E   Can you describe what happened when you fell?
3   A   Which injuries are causing you the most discomfort?
4   F   Are you taking any regular medication at the moment?
5   D   Do you need some pain relief?

ACCIDENT and EMERGENCY- Patient 2

1   E   How old is your child?
2   D   Why have you brought her to the hospital today?
3   A   Has she been stung by an ant before?
4   B   Can you describe her reaction today?
5   C   Was her breathing affected?

Practice 2: Forming appropriate questions

0	1	2	3	4	5	6	7	8	9	10	11	12	13	14	15
J	I	D	G	B	N	O	L	H	A	K	C	F	P	E	M

Practice 3: Forming questions and choosing appropriate answers

NURSING POSITION INTERVIEW

0   Question: **Why did you decide to become a nurse?**
    Answer: **F   Because I have always been interested in helping sick people.**

1   Question: How long have you been a nurse?
    Answer: **E**   About 4 years.

2   Question: What do you like most about working as a nurse?
    Answer: **G**   I really enjoy the challenge of working with many different people.

3   Question: What personal qualities and skills would you bring to this position?
    Answer: **D**   I am hard-working, enjoy helping people and have relevant nursing experience.

4   Question: Do you plan to specialise in any particular area in the future?
    Answer: **C**   Yes, I would like to learn more about diabetes management.

5	Question:	How do you learn about the latest advances in nursing?
	Answer:	**A** By reading reports and by attending seminars in the field.
6	Question:	What are your long-term professional goals?
	Answer:	**B** To establish a diabetes education clinic in my local community.

Practice 4: Identifying key words in questions and choosing appropriate answers.

0	1	2	3	4	5	6	7	8
B	A	C	C	A	B	B	C	B

Practice 5: Identifying key words in answers and choosing appropriate questions

0	1	2	3	4	5	6	7	8
B	C	A	A	C	B	B	C	A

UNIT 2 COUNTABLE AND UNCOUNTABLE NOUNS

Practice 1: Identifying countable and uncountable nouns 1

COUNTABLE	UNCOUNTABLE	BOTH
dentist	vitamin B	pain
tumour	calcium	hair
syringe	diverticulitis	medication
prescription	acne	bone
thermometer		
nebuliser		
mask		
lung		
cell		

Practice 2: Identifying countable and uncountable nouns 2

Pre-operative preparation

0 **c, u**

1 c

2 u, u

3 c, u

Cardiac rehabilitation

1 u, c, c

2 c

3 u, u

4 c

Practice 3: Choosing appropriate follow-on sentences

0	1	2	3	4	5	6	7	8	9	10	11	12
K	D	A	G	M	B	C	E	F	L	I	J	H

UNIT 3 ARTICLES

Practice 1: Matching functions of a and an

0   B

1   D

2   C

3   E

4   A

Practice 2: Matching functions of the

1   A

2   D

3   C

4   B

5   E

Practice 3: Matching functions of nouns without articles

1   B

2   E

3   H

4   C

5   A

6   G

7   F

8   D

Practice 4: Complete the sentence

0	---	10	the
1	the / a	11	---, ---, the
2	a	12	A
3	---	13	---
4	a	14	an
5	---	15	the
6	---	16	---
7	the	17	---
8	The	18	the
9	an		

Practice 5: Error correction

0 Mrs Jones is in **the** pain.

1 If your symptoms persist, please see your doctor for **an** advice.

2 He is making **a** good progress after the surgery.

3 That is **a** very strange behaviour for him.

4 **The** life with a disability can be difficult.

5 He would like to work as a nurse in **the** Melbourne.

6 Have you had **the** lunch, yet?

Practice 6: Cloze

0 **a**

1 an

2 ---

3 a

4 A/The

5 the

6 a

7 ---

8 ---

9 the

10 the

UNIT 4   DETERMINERS AND QUANTITIES

Practice 1: Complete the sentence 1

Any or **some**?

0 **any**

1 some

2 any

3 some

4 any

5 any

Much or **many**?

1 many

2 much

3 much

4 many

5 much

Few or **little**?

1 little

2 few

3 few

4 little

A **few** or a **little**?

1 a few

2 a little

3 a few

4 a little

Practice 2: Complete the sentence 2

0 <u>All</u>

1 many

2 None

3 all

4 any

5 No

6 Few

7 any

8 much

9 Every

10 Some

11 a little

12 many

Practice 3: Multiple choice cloze

0 B all

1 C much

2 D a few

3 A little

4 B many

5 B Some

6 A many

7 B any

8 A a few

9 D No

10 C any

Practice 4: Matching questions and responses

0	1	2	3	4	5	6	7	8	9	10	11	12	13	14
D	E	F	G	N	I	K	B	A	C	J	L	O	M	H

Practice 5: Complete the sentence

Example	Passage A	0 °C

Answers Passages A-L

Passage A	1	beats	2	breaths						
Passage B	1	times	2	millilitres	3	minute	4	hours		
Passage C	1	grams	2	centimetres	3	centimetres	4	percentile		
Passage D	1	days	2	day	3	puffs				
Passage E	1	millimetres	2	beats	3	weeks				
Passage F	1	millilitres	2	dose	3	seconds	4	times		
Passage G	1	packet	2	roll	3	sachets	4	tube	5	vials
Passage H	1	centimetre	2	times	3	hourly	4	days		
Passage I	1	year	2	kilograms	3	millilitres	4	hours	5	times
Passage J	1	drops	2	minutes	3	days				
Passage K	1	months	2	scoops	3	millilitres	4	day		
Passage L	1	sachet	2	millilitres	3	minutes				

UNIT 5   VERBS: PAST, PRESENT AND FUTURE

Practice 1: Matching functions of verb tenses 1

0   A

1   G

2   E

3   C

4   H

5   F

6   B

7   D

Practice 2: Matching functions of verb tenses 2

0   F

1   B

2   C

3   A

4   E

5   D

Practice 3: Matching functions with verb tenses 3

0   C

1   A

2   B

3   D

4   F

5   G

6   E

Practice 4: Error Correction

00 **has**

0 ✔

1 ✔

2 has

3 did

4 being

5 ✔

6 been

7 ✔

8 had

9 ✔

10 was

11 to

12 be

13 will

14 to

15 ✔

Practice 5: Sentence transformation

0 She has **not seen the oncologist for** 2 months.

1 The doctor **is going to make** a small incision to remove your splinter.

2 Jack Nichols sustained a groin strain **while he was playing** a game of hockey.

3 Amber Ling has **been taking this medication for** 6 weeks.

4 **How long have you been** using your inhaler without a spacer?

5 She **has not had** a febrile seizure before.

6 She was referred to a vascular surgeon because a **venous blood clot had formed** in her right lower leg.

7 When the social worker **arrived, the family had gone** home.

8 Quick! She **is going to** faint.

9 Felicity Singh **had a fall** at 11.45 this morning and fractured her femur.

10 The clinic **closes at** 1pm on Saturdays.

Practice 6: Multiple choice cloze

Letter 1

0 **A**

1 C

2 B

3 B

4 A

5 C

1   C
2   B
3   C
4   B
5   A

UNIT 6   PASSIVES

Practice 1: Complete the sentence

0   F   **will be inducted**
1   C   were cancelled
2   G   have been rescheduled
3   A   has been misplaced
4   H   will no longer be served
5   B   are to be taken
6   E   need reminding
7   D   have their teeth checked

Practice 2: Error correction

00 was

0   ✔
1   ✔
2   was
3   been
4   ✔
5   ✔
6   been
7   be
8   ✔
9   ✔
10 been
11 ✔
12 been

Practice 3: Complete the sentence

0   These pills **must be taken** with food.
1   Mr Kapoor **was discharged** this morning.
2   How often does **this dressing need to be** changed?
3   The new bone **will be held** in place with screws and a metal plate.
4   Millie Goodwin **has not been given** any pain relief yet.

5   The skin cancer on his ear **is going to be removed** by a plastic surgeon tomorrow.

6   Mr Douglas **has been diagnosed with** kidney stones.

7   **Have** Mr Almeida's inhalers **been ordered** from the pharmacy yet?

8   Have you ever **had** your skin **checked by** a dermatologist ?

9   The wound **had not been cleaned properly** and an infection developed.

10 Ms Lee **was admitted to hospital with** acute abdominal pain.

11 It **is recommended that** people have a tetanus booster shot every ten years.

12 Please wait here Mr Kennedy. Mrs Kennedy **is being treated** for shock and minor cuts and abrasions.

Practice 4: Multiple choice cloze

0	1	2	3	4	5	6	7	8	9	10
C	B	C	A	B	B	A	B	C	A	C

UNIT 7   CONDITIONALS

Practice 1: Matching conditional sentences with their meaning

0	1	2	3	4	5	6	7
B	A	B	A	A	A	B	B
D	D	D	C	C	D	C	C

Practice 2: Sentence completion

0	1	2	3	4	5	6	7	8	9
A	B	A	B	A	C	B	A	C	B

Practice 3: Sentence completion

0	1	2	3	4	5	6
B	D	F	C	G	A	E

Practice 4: Complete the sentence

0   unless

1   if

2   provided (that) / as long as

3   provided (that) / as long as /if

4   in case

5   Provided (that) / As long as /If

Practice 5: Sentence transformation

0   Mrs Fielding <u>**wishes she could remember**</u> simple things.

1   Do not get out of bed without assistance **in case you have** a fall.

2   I would not have run out of medication **if I had asked** the doctor for a new prescription.

3   Do **not use this inhaler unless** you are feeling breathless.

4   Mr Patel would **not be in hospital if** he had not broken his hip.

5   I **wish I had not taken** that supplement without asking for the doctor's advice. I feel terrible!

6   Your skin will burn **unless you protect** yourself against the sun.

7   You can stay in your own home **as long as you have** daily visits from a nurse.

8   Your recovery would be faster **if you did your exercises** every day.

9   We will be able to operate this afternoon **provided her condition does not** deteriorate.

10 I will give you a repeat for this prescription **in case your infection** needs further treatment.

UNIT 8   DEPENDENT PREPOSITIONS

Practice 1: Matching sentence beginnings and endings

0	1	2	3	4	5	6	7	8
E	A	I	D	B	H	C	G	F

Practice 2: Complete the sentence - adjective + preposition

0   **dependent on**

1   deficient **in**

2   capable **of**

3   eligible **for**

4   immune **to**

5   detrimental **to**

6   full **of**

7   indicative **of**

8   concerned **about**

9   susceptible **to**

10 compatible **with**

11 ready **for**

12 low **in**

13 worried **about**

14 receptive **to**

15 upset **about**

16 responsible **for**

Practice 3: Matching sentence beginnings and endings

0	1	2	3	4	5	6	7	8	9
I	C	A	B	G	D	E	F	J	H

Practice 4: Complete the sentence - verb + preposition

0   **for**

1   with

2   to

3   from

4   to

5   on

6   on

7   to

8   with

9   with

10 from

11 from

12 to

13 with

14 from

15 with

16 against

Practice 5: Cloze

0   of

1   with

2   to

3   with

4   of

5   in

6   to

7   in

8   with

9   on

10 in

Practice 6: Multiple choice cloze

0   B   assist

1   C   different

2   A   prevent

3   C   suitable

4   C   depends

5   A   consult

6   B   adjust

7   A   anxious

8   C   listen

9   A   refrain

10 B   focus

11 A   specialises

12 C   referred

UNIT 9   WORD FORMATION

Practice 1: Identifying verbs, nouns and adjectives

0   appendicitis – NOUN

1   dilate – VERB
2   aggressive – ADJECTIVE
3   palliative – ADJECTIVE
4   strenuous – ADJECTIVE
5   orthodontist – NOUN
6   alleviate - VERB

7   astigmatism - NOUN
8   notify - VERB
9   hypertension - NOUN
10   prognosis - NOUN
11   macular - ADJECTIVE
12   infectious - ADJECTIVE

Practice 2: adjective or noun?

0   safety

1   infection / redness / tenderness
2   allergic
3   dental / surgery
4   pharmacist / pharmacy / pharmaceutical
5   Bacterial

Practice 3: verb or noun?

0   A   dress

1   B   obstruction
2   B   urination
3   A   improve
4   B   referral

5   A   diagnose
6   A   observe
7   B   prescription
8   B   admission

Practice 4: verb, noun or adjective?

0   useful

1   informative
2   rehabilitation
3   customised
4   recovery
5   arrival
6   professional
7   independence
8   expectations
9   anxious

10   depressed
11   motivated
12   helpful
13   advice
14   healthy
15   connected
16   information
17   assistance

Practice 5: Transforming word forms - adjectives and adverbs

0   angry   angrily
00 irresponsible   **irresponsibly**
1   accidental   **accidentally**
2   anxious   **anxiously**

3	final	**finally**
4	**independent**	independently
5	unexpected	**unexpectedly**
6	**usual**	usually
7	**comfortable**	comfortably
8	hungry	**hungrily**
9	**tender**	tenderly
10	psychological	**psychologically**
11	**surgical**	surgically
12	painful	**painfully**

Practice 6: adjective or adverb?.

0   B regularly

1   B   orally
2   A   significant
3   B   recently

4   A   Annual
5   A   serious
6   B   sparingly

Practice 7: Using prefixes

0   intravenous

00 postoperative

1   immaturity
2   malnutrition
3   defibrillator
4   miscarriage
5   infertile

6   preeclampsia
7   unconscious
8   transmission
9   anticoagulant
10 hyperallergenic

Practice 8: Complete the sentence

0   antibiotics

1   transfusion
2   Antenatal
3   incontinence
4   irregularly
5   unassisted

6   Atypical
7   transplant
8   dehydrated
9   vaccinations
10 hypotension

Practice 9: Word formation

0   detection

1   generally
2   survival
3   exposure
4   abnormal
5   uncontrollably
6   protective
7   playing
8   regularly

9   appearance
10 unusual
11 pathologist
12 analysis
13 removal
14 surrounding
15 treatments
16 untreated

UNIT 10 REVIEW

Practice 1: Matching questions and answers

0	1	2	3	4	5	6	7	8	9	10
D	G	K	F	B	I	H	E	A	J	C

Practice 2: Complete the sentence

Letter 1

0 **had**

1 the

2 an

3 on

4 some

5 is

6 regular

7 had

8 hours

9 concerns

10 Provided

Letter 2

11 was

12 was

13 complications

14 other

15 am

16 to

Practice 3: Multiple choice cloze

Text 1: Blood specimen collection

0 B the

1 B has

2 C If

3 B completed

4 C Inform

5 A is

6 A considered

7 C for

8 A is

9 B from

10 C all

11 B any

12 A contaminated

Text 2: Letter of Discharge

0   C **being**

1   A to

2   C a fall

3   A alone

4   B independent

5   B has meals delivered

6   A contacts

7   A bruising

8   B to

9   C No

10 A hours

11 A with

12 C has been referred

13 C has trialled

14 B If

15 B assessment

16 C information

Practice 4: Sentence transformation

0   Mrs Kendall <u>**needs to be evaluated by**</u> a psychiatrist.

1   I **have never had problems** with this medication before.

2   She will have to go to hospital **if she does not gain** weight.

3   The decision **will be made by** the surgical team tomorrow.

4   Take your scans to your appointment **in case the doctor asks** to see them.

5   It **has been 5 weeks since** Mr Johnson last had a spasm in his lower back.

6   Can you rate your **pain on a scale of** 1 to 10?

7   When **did you first** notice these symptoms?

8   How **much does your baby weigh**?

9   She **was low in** potassium due to an episode of acute gastroenteritis.

10 If I had not been vomiting all night, I **would have gone** to work.

11 You will **have a urinary catheter inserted** during surgery.

12 His condition **is being closely monitored** following the infection.

Practice 5: Error correction

Text 1: Professional development seminar: Medication adherence - a case study

0   a

1   has

2   ✔

3 been

4 ✔

5 being

6 What

7 an

8 ✔

9 If

10 not

11 ✔

12 with

13 the

14 ✔

Text 2: Patient summary

0 ✔

1 was

2 a

3 ✔

4 on

5 ✔

6 has

7 provided

8 an

9 another

10 ✔

11 ✔

Practice 6: Word formation

0 **presented**

1 diagnosis

2 generally

3 abdominal

4 examination

5 mildly

6 management

7 discussed

8 viral

9 instructions

10 worsen

Printed in the USA
CPSIA information can be obtained
at www.ICGtesting.com
CBHW061534260724
12249CB00022B/533